MATERIALS SCIENCE AND TECHNOLOGIES

MATERIALS SCIENCE RESEARCHER BIOGRAPHICAL SKETCHES AND RESEARCH SUMMARIES

MATERIALS SCIENCE AND TECHNOLOGIES

Additional books in this series can be found on Nova's website
under the Series tab.

Additional E-books in this series can be found on Nova's website
under the E-book tab.

MATERIALS SCIENCE AND TECHNOLOGIES

MATERIALS SCIENCE RESEARCHER BIOGRAPHICAL SKETCHES AND RESEARCH SUMMARIES

SATOMI MATSUMOTO

AND

UEDA IWATE

EDITORS

Nova Science Publishers, Inc.

New York

For permission to use material from this book please contact us:
Telephone 631-231-7269; Fax 631-231-8175
Web Site: http://www.novapublishers.com

NOTICE TO THE READER

The Publisher has taken reasonable care in the preparation of this book, but makes no expressed or implied warranty of any kind and assumes no responsibility for any errors or omissions. No liability is assumed for incidental or consequential damages in connection with or arising out of information contained in this book. The Publisher shall not be liable for any special, consequential, or exemplary damages resulting, in whole or in part, from the readers' use of, or reliance upon, this material. Any parts of this book based on government reports are so indicated and copyright is claimed for those parts to the extent applicable to compilations of such works.

Independent verification should be sought for any data, advice or recommendations contained in this book. In addition, no responsibility is assumed by the publisher for any injury and/or damage to persons or property arising from any methods, products, instructions, ideas or otherwise contained in this publication.

This publication is designed to provide accurate and authoritative information with regard to the subject matter covered herein. It is sold with the clear understanding that the Publisher is not engaged in rendering legal or any other professional services. If legal or any other expert assistance is required, the services of a competent person should be sought. FROM A DECLARATION OF PARTICIPANTS JOINTLY ADOPTED BY A COMMITTEE OF THE AMERICAN BAR ASSOCIATION AND A COMMITTEE OF PUBLISHERS.

Additional color graphics may be available in the e-book version of this book.

Library of Congress Cataloging-in-Publication Data

Materials science researcher biographical sketches and research summaries / editors, Satomi Matsumoto and Ueda Iwate.
      p. cm.
 Includes bibliographical references and index.
 ISBN 978-1-61942-153-0 (hardcover)
 1. Materials science. 2. Materials scientists--Biography. I. Matsumoto, Satomi. II. Iwate, Ueda.
 TA145.M38 2011
 620.1'1--dc23
                              2011043193

Published by Nova Science Publishers, Inc. † *New York*

CONTENTS

PREFACE

This new book compiles biographical sketches of top professionals in the field of materials science, as well as research summaries from a number of different focuses in this important field.

PART 1 – RESEARCH BIOGRAPHIES

In: Materials Science Researcher Biographical Sketches …   ISBN: 978-1-61942-153-0
Editors: Satomi Matsumoto and Ueda Iwate   © 2013 Nova Science Publishers, Inc.

Chapter 1

BIOGRAPHICAL SKETCH

Raju Adhikari, PhD

Affiliation: CSIRO Materials Science and Engineering

Date of Birth: 24/02/1958

Address: Bag 10, CSIRO Materials Science and Engineering

Research and Professional Experience

Design and Synthesis of Polymers for Biomedical and Tissue Engineering applications

Professional Appointments

Principal Research Scientist

Honors

CSIRO medal for research innovation 2006

Publications during last three years

Pathiraja A. Gunatillake and **Raju Adhikari;** Biodegradable Polyurethanes: Design, Synthesis, Properties and Potential Applications. *Nova Science Publishers, Inc,* 400 Oser Avenue, Suite 1600 Hauppauge, NY 11788-3619, USA, 2011

Raju Adhikari; Buu Dao; Jonathan Hodgkin; James Mardel **(2011),** Synthesis, structures and membrane properties of siloxane-imide co-polymers produced by aqueous polymerization, European Polymer Journal Volume 47, Issue 6, June 2011, Pages 1328-1337

Matthias H€aussler, Y. Phei Lok, Ming Chen, Jacek Jasieniak, **Raju Adhikari,** Simon P. King, Saif A. Hague, Craig M. Forsyth, Kevin Winzenberg, Scott E. Watkins, Ezio Rizzardo and Gerard J. Wilson **(2010)** Benzothiadiazole-Containing Pendant Polymers Prepared by RAFT and Their Electro-Optical Properties, Macromolecules 2010, 43, 7101-7110

M. Jayasundera a, B. Adhikari, **R. Adhikari,** P. Aldred, **(2010)** The effect of protein types and low molecular weight surfactants on spray drying of sugar-rich foods, Food Hydrocolloids 25 (2011) 459e469

J.A. Werkmeister, T.A. Tebb' **R. Adhikari,** T. Le, H.C. Taing, J.F. White **(2010),** Biodegradable and injectable cure-on-demand polyurethane scaffolds for regeneration of articular cartilage, R. Mayadunne, P.A. Gunatillake, S.J. Danon, M.D.M Evans and J.A.M. Ramshaw, Acta Biomaterialia 6 (2010) 3471-3481

Mithila Jayasundera & Benu P. Adhikari, **Raju Adhikari &** Peter Aldred **(2010),** The Effect of Food-Grade Low-Molecular-Weight Surfactants and Sodium Caseinate on Spray Drying of Sugar-Rich Foods, Food Biophysics; 2010, s11483-010-9153-4

Raju Adhikari, Stephen J. Danon, Penny Bean, Tam Le, Pathiraja Gunatillake, John A. M. Ramshaw, Jerome A. Werkmeister **(2010),** Evaluation of in situ curable biodegradable polyurethanes bcontaining zwitterion components, J Mater Sci: Mater Med, **2010,** s10856-009-3955-2

Raju Adhikari, Pathiraja. A. Gunatillake, Ian Griffiths, Lisa Tatai, Malsha Wickramaratna, Shadi. Houshyar, Tim Moore, Roshan TM. Mayadunne, John Field, Margaret McGee and Tanai Carbone **(2008)** Biodegradable Injectable Polyurethanes: Synthesis and Evaluation for Orthopedic Application, Biomaterials, 29 (2008) 3762-3770

John R. Field, Pathiraja Gunatillake, **Raju Adhikari,** John A.M. Ramshaw, Jerome A. Werkmeister model **(2008)** The use of biodegradable urethane-based adhesives to appose meniscal defect edges: a preliminary study in an ovine, Aus Vet Journal, 86, 229-234.

In: Materials Science Researcher Biographical Sketches ...   ISBN: 978-1-61942-153-0

Editors: Satomi Matsumoto and Ueda Iwate   © 2013 Nova Science Publishers, Inc.

Chapter 2

BIOGRAPHICAL SKETCH

Maria do Carmo de Barros Pimentel

Date of Birth: 22 June 1956

Education

Institution and Location	Degree	Year Conferred	Scientific Field
Dept. of Chemistry Engineering in the Universidade Federal de Pernambuco (Brazil) in Organic Chemistry	Graduation – Bachelor	1974 – 1977	Industrial Chemistry
Dept. of Biochemistry in the Universidade Federal de Pernambuco – Brazil (Enzymology and Microbiology)	Post-Graduation	1979 – 1983	Master in Biochemistry
Universidade Estadual de Campinas – São Paulo – Brazil (Biological Chemistry – Bioprocess using enzyme) Under the supervision of Dr. Nelson Duran	Post – Graduation – PhD	1994 – 1996	Chemistry
International Training Programme (ITP) – GBF - Germany Industrial Biotechnology Project: Receptor purificação under the supervision of Dr. Helen Stajer		1996	
Post-Doctorial Training at University of Cambridge – UK Institute of Biotechnology Project: Cloning, Expression and Purification of Spore Cortex-Lytic Enzymes under supervision of Prof. Christopher R. Lowe		2003 – 2004	

Contact Points

Address:
Rua José Carvalheira 35/1702 - Tamarineira
52051-060 – Recife – PE – Brasil
Telephone: (+55) 81 3266 0644 or (+55) 81 9961 3893 (mobile phone)
E-mail: barros_carneiro@hotmail.com

Professional Address

Departamento de Bioquímica and Laboratório de Imunopatologia Keizo Asami (LIKA) at Universidade Federal Pernambuco – Av. Prof. Moraes Rego s/n, Cidade Universitária, 50670-901 - Recife – Pernambuco – Brasil.

1. Professional Activities

1985 – 1990:	Lecturer in General Chemistry in Polytechnic School
	Universidade de Pernambuco – FESP
1986 – 1996:	Assistant Professor in Biochemistry
	(Graduation and Master in Biochemistry Courses)
1997 – 2009:	Adjunct Professor in Biochemistry
	(Graduation and Master in Biochemistry Courses)
2010 – present:	Associate Professor in Biochemistry
	(Graduation and Master in Biochemistry Courses)
	Dept. Biochemistry – Universidade Federal de Pernambuco
1997 – present:	Scientific Consultant of HEBRON – Chemical and
	Pharmaceutical Industry – Recife – Brazil

2. International Links

1998:	Technical visit at Universidade do Porto - Portugal
	Faculty of Pharmacy – Dept. of Physico-Chemistry
	Dr. Maria da Conceição Montenegro Branco
	(Biossensor for lactate using Electrodes ions selective)
2000:	Technical visit at University of Birmingham - UK
	Chemobiotec Laboratories – Prof. John Kennedy
2001:	Technical visit at University of Birmingham - UK
	Chemobiotec Laboratories – Prof. John Kennedy
	(Biossensor for sucrose – Project on Diversification of sugar
	cane products – British Council – CAPES – University of Birmingham)
1995 – 1999:	University of St. Andrews – Scotland
	(Supervisor of students of the Programme ERASMO)
	Prof. William Ledingham

3. Scientific Projects

1999 – 2001:	Project: Optimization and diversification of sugar cane industries in the Northeastern of Brazil Granted by British Council – CAPES
2000 – present:	Project: A new economical perspective for sugar industry: production of fructose syrup and proteins for feed Granted by FINEP – Sugar Industry
2002 – present:	Project: Development of national technology for pharmaceutical industry Granted by FINEP – Pharmaceutical Industry
2000 – present:	Project: Biossensor using electrodes ion selective Granted by CAPES – Portugal

4. Publications

Patent:

Pabyton G. Cadena; Alberto N. Araújo; Maria C. Montenegro; Maria C. Pimentel; José L. Lima Filho; Valdinete L. Silva. Product formulation for Kit Reagent to Lipophilic Molecules. **221105687036** – National Institute of Industrial Properties in Brazil, 2011.

1) Pabyton G. Cadena, Frank N. Wiggers, Roberto A. Silva, José L. Lima Filho, Maria C.B. Pimentel. Kinetics and bioreactor studies of immobilized invertase on polyurethane rigid adhesive foam. Bioresource Technology, v. 102, p. 513–518, 2011.

2) Pabyton G. Cadena; Alberto N. Araújo; Maria C. Montenegro; Maria C. Pimentel; José L. Lima Filho; Valdinete L. Silva. Physical-Chemical Parameters and Validation of a Colorimetric Method for Deoxycholic and Ursodeoxycholic Acids: Kit Reagent and Optical Sensor. Chemistry and Physics of Lipids, v. 164, p. 99-105, 2011.

3) P.G. Cadena; R.A.S. Jeronimo; J.M. Melo; R.A. Silva; J.L. Lima Filho; M.C.B. Pimentel. Covalent immobilization of invertase on polyurethane, plast film and ferromagnetic dacron. Bioresourse Technology, 110:1595-1602, 2010.

4) Pabyton G. Cadena; Eric C. Oliveira; Alberto N. Araújo; Maria C.B.S.M. Montenegro; Maria C.B. Pimentel; José L.Lima Filho; Valdinete L. Silva. Simple Determination of Deoxycholic and Ursodeoxycholic Acids by Phenolphtalein-□-Cyclodextrin Inclusion Complex. Lipids, v. 44, p. 1063-1070, 2009.

5) Pimentel, M.C.B., Leão, A. B. F., Melo, E. H. M., Ledingham, W. M., Lima Filho, J. L., Sivewright, M., Kennedy, J. F. Immobilization of Candida rugosa lipase on Magnetized Dacron: Kinetic Study. Artificial Cells, Blood Substitutes, and Biotechnology: An International Journal, 35:221 – 235, 2007.

6) Kennedy, J. F., Pimentel, M.C.B., Melo, E. H. M., Lima-Filho, J.L. Sucrose biosensor as an alternative tool for sugarcane field samples. Journal of the Science of Food and Agriculture, 87:2266-2271, 2007.

7) Pimentel, M.C.B., Leão, A.B.F., Melo, E.H.M., Ledingham, W.M., Lima Filho, J.L., Kennedy, J.F. Immobilization of *Penicillium citrinum* Lipase on Ferromagnetic Azide-dacron. Biotechnol. 5 (3), 228-233, 2006.

8) Moraes, M. C., Pimentel, M. C. B., Moraes, M., Lima Filho, J. L. Production of an extracellular polysaccharide with emulsifier properties by *Penicillium citrinum*. World Journal of Microbiology & Biotechnology. Netherlands: v.18, p.230 - 233, 2002.

9) Silva, V. L., Oliveira, M. I. P., Pimentel, M. C. B., Montenegro, M. C., ARAUJO, A. N.L-Glutamate determination in food samples by flow injection analysis. Analytical Chimica Acta. USA:, v.65, p.75 - 78, 2001.

10) Knight, K., Pimentel, M. C. B., Camargodemorais, M. M., Ledingham, W., LIMA Filho, J. L., Maia, M. D. D. Immobilization of lipase from *Fusarium solani* FS1. Brazilian Journal of Microbiology. São Paulo:, v.31, n.3, p.1 - 6, 2000.

11) Miranda, O., Salgueio, A. A., Pimentel, M. C. B., Lima Filho, J. L., Melo, E. H. M., Durán, N. Lipase production by a Brazilian strain of *Penicillium citrinum* using an industrial residue. AAPG Memoir. Grã-Bretanha:, v.69, p.145 - 147, 1999.

12) Pimentel, M. C. B., melo, E. H. M., Lima Filho, J. L., Ledingham, W., DURÁN, N. Lipase from a Brazilian strain *Penicillium citrinum* cultured in a simple and inexpensive medium:heat-denaturation, kinetics and pH stability. Applied Biochemistry and Biotechnology. Estados Unidos:, v.66, p.185 - 195, 1997.

13) Rodrigues, M. S. M., Pimentel, M. C. B., Silva, N. H., Melo, E. H. M., Durán, N. Behavior of pitch in pulp mills by *Candida rugosa* lipase. Proceedings Of The Fourth Brazilian Symposium On Chemistry Of Lignins. Brasil:, v.5, p.219 - 222, 1996. The editors of Proceedings registered in Chemical Abstract: Eduardo H. Magalhães Melo; Maria do Carmo de Barros Pimentel; Alexandra Amorim Salgueiro; Cesar Augusto M. Abreu.

14) Pimentel, M. C. B., Melo, E. H. M., Lima Filho, J. L., Durán, N. Production of lipase free of citrinin by *Penicillium citrrinum*. Mycopathology. Netherlands:, v.133, p.119 - 121, 1996.

15) Leite, V., Leão, I. C., Pimentel, M. C. B., Silva, V. L., Melo, E. H. M., LIMA Filho, J. L. Simple and inexpensive flow injection analysis for determination of sucrose using invertase and glucose oxidase immobilised on glass beads. Biotechnology Techniques. USA:, v.9, n.5, p.345 - 348, 1995.

16) Nadruz, W., Leão, I. C., Ledingham, W., Melo, E. H. M., Krieger, N., Pimentel, M. C. B., Kennedy, J. Characterization of Candida rugosa lipase immobilised on alkymie glass beads. The Genetic Engineer And Biotechnologist. Inglaterra:, v.14, n.3, p.143 - 148, 1994.

17) Pimentel, M. C. B., Krieger, N., Coelho, L. C. C., Fontana, J. D., Melo, E. H. M., Ledingham, W., Lima Filho, J. L. Lipase from a Brazilian strain of *Penicillium citrinum*. Applied Biochemistry and Biotechnology. Estados Unidos:, v.49, p.59 - 74, 1994.

18) Pimentel, M. C. B., Ferreira, M. S. S., ARAÚJO, C. Screening, thermal properties and production yam extract of fungal sucrose phodphorylase. Applied Biochemistry and Biotechnology. p.199 - 205, 1992.

19) Pimentel, M. C. B., Ferreira, M. S. S. Immobilized sucrose phosphorylase from *Leuconostoc mesenteroides*. Applied Biochemistry and Biotechnology. USA:, v.27, n.1, p.37 - 44, 1991.

20) Melo, E. H. M., Lima Filho, J. L., Pimentel, M. C. B., Kennedy, J. F. Banana Stalk:an alternative source for pulp in Northeast of Brazil In: International Symposium on the Bioconversion of Renewable Raw Materials, Braunschweig. Gesellschat für Biotechnologische Forschung mbH - GBF, v.1. p.75 – 77,2000.

In: Materials Science Researcher Biographical Sketches ...   ISBN: 978-1-61942-153-0
Editors: Satomi Matsumoto and Ueda Iwate   © 2013 Nova Science Publishers, Inc.

Chapter 3

BIOGRAPHICAL SKETCH

Chunxiang Cui, Professor

Affiliation: Director of center of material research in Hebei province, Director of School of Materials Science and Technology in Hebei University of Technology

Date of Birth: Feb. 17, 1958

Education

Institution and Location	Degree	Year Conferred	Scientific Field
	Ph.D		

Contact Points: Prof. Dr. Chunxiang CUI, School of Materials Science and Engineering, Hebei University of Technology, No.8, Road No, 1 Dingzigu, Tianjin 300130 P.R. China

Professional Appointments

Nano ceramic particles reinforced Al matrix composites, Nano-Magnetic Materials, In situ $K_2Ti_6O_{13}$/Ti biology materials.

Honors

1995.6-present: Director, Society of Material Science for China Society of Metals
1996.10-present: Director, Society for Metals of Tianjin
1997.11-present: Member in New York Academy of Sciences (USA)

Publications during last three years

A) Books

1) Cui Chunxiang, The synthesis and fabrication of Materails (Materials Science and Engineering Graduate teaching book), bone cells, ed, East China University of Technology Press, Shanghai, January 2010

2) Biocompatibility and fabrication of *in situ* bioceremic coating/titanium alloy Biocomposites, C. Cui, Hebei University of Technology, China, Woodhead Publishing Limited, 2010, CRC Press Woodhead Publishing ISBN 978-1-84569-434-0 (book)

B) Articles in Journals

1) Lizhen Zhao Chunxiang Cui*, Growth Characteristics and Corrosion Resistance of Micro-arc Oxidation Coating on Pure Magnesium for Biomedical Applications, Corrosion Science. 52 (2010), pp. 2228-2234.

2) Wang, Q.Z.; Cui, C.X*.; Lu, D.M.; Bu, S.J.,Fabrication and properties of a novel ZnO/Cu composite, Journal of Materials Processing Technology, v 210, n 3, p 497-503, February 1, 2010.

3) Wang, Q.Z.; Cui, C.X*.; Liu, S.J.; Zhao, L.C. Open-celled porous Cu prepared by replication of NaCl space-holders, Materials Science and Engineering A, v 527, n 4-5, p 1275-1278, February 15, 2010.

4) Wei Yang, Chunxiang Cui*, Jibing Sun and Baoli Wang, Fabrication and magnetic properties of Fe_3Co_7 alloy nanowire arrays, Journal of Materials Science, Vo.45,2010(6) 1523-1527, DOI: 10.1007/s10853-009-4116-1.

5) Ji-Bing Sun, Dan Han, Chun-Xiang Cui, Wei Yang, Liang Li, Fan Yang, Effects of quenching speeds on microstructure and magnetic properties of novel $SmCo_{6.9}Hf_{0.1}(CNTs)_{0.05}$ melt-spun ribbons, Acta Materialia, Volume 57, Issue 9, May 2009, Pages 2845-2850.

6) Ji-Bing Sun, A. Javed, Zhe-Xu Zhang, Chun-Xiang Cui, Miao-Xin Zhang, Rui-Ping Han, Effect of B addition on the microstructure and magnetic properties of melt-spun $Sm_{12}Co_{60\ x}Fe_{19}Cu_6Zr_3B_x$ (0 x 3) ribbons, Materials Science and Engineering: B, Volume 167, Issue 2, 15 March 2010, Pages 102-106.

7) Zhao, Lichen; Cui, Chunxiang*; Liu, Shuangjin; Qi, Yumin, Influence of in situ MgO coating on corrosion resistance of pure magnesium in normal saline, Advanced Materials Research, vol 79-82, 2009, p 1039-1042.

8) Ji-Bing Sun, Dan Han, Chun-Xiang Cui, Wei Yang, Hao Zhou, Rui-Ting Tian, Li-Guo Yang, Effects of Hf and CNTs on magnetic transformation and thermal stabilities of $TbCu_7$-type Sm–Co matrix ribbon magnets, Journal of Alloys and Compounds, Volume 487, Issues 1-2, 13 November 2009, Pages 626-630.

9) Ji-bing Sun, Zhe-xu Zhang, Chun-xiang Cui, Wei Yang, Liang Li, Dan Han, Li-guo Yang, Li-jie Li, $Sm_{12}Co_{59}Cu_6Fe_{20}Zr_3$ sintered magnets made from as-cast alloy and melt-spun ribbons, Journal of Alloys and Compounds, Volume 486, Issues 1-2, 3 November 2009, Pages 819-823.

10) Chunxiang Cui*, Ling Bai, Qingzhou Wang, Shaojing Bu and Yumin Qi Fabrication of Ti-based amorphous composite and biocompatibility research Journal of Wuhan University of Technology--Materials Science Edition, Vol. 25, 2010(1)8-11.

11) Wang Tiebao, Cui Chunxiang, Wang Xiaodong, and Li Guobin, Fabrication of Nano-CeO2 and Application of Nano-CeO2 in Fe Matrix Composites, Journal of Nanomaterials, 2010(2010)1-5, doi:10.1155/2010/768251.

12) Chunxiang Cui, BaoMin Hu, Lichen Zhao, Shuangjin Liu, Titanium alloy production technology, market prospects and industry development, Materials & Design, vol.32, 2010: 1684–1691.

13) Xue, Xuelian; Cui, Chunxiang; Liu, Lijun; Qi, Yumin, Preparation and mechanical properties of Ti12Zr10Si5Fe2Sn amorphous alloys, Rare Metal Materials and Engineering, v 39, n 7, p 1248-1250, July 2010.

14) Cui Chunxiang, Guo Ping, Sun Jibing, Yang Wei, Fabrication and magnetic properties of Fe3Pt /Sm2Fe17Nx/ -Fe composite, processings of 11[Th] Joint MMM-Intermag Conference, P 215, Washingdon, DC, January 18-22,2010.

15) Wei Yang, Chunxiang Cui, Jibing Sun and Baoli Wang, Fabrication and magnetic properties of Fe_3Co_7 alloy nanowire arrays, Journal of Materials Science, *Vo.45,2010(6)* 1523-1527.

16) Wang, Q.Z.; Cui, C.X.; Liu, S.J.; Zhao, L.C. Open-celled porous Cu prepared by replication of NaCl space-holders, Materials Science and Engineering A, v 527, n 4-5, p 1275-1278.

17) Ji-bing Sun, Zhe-xu Zhang, Chun-xiang Cui, Wei Yang, Liang Li, Dan Han, Li-guo Yang, Li-jie Li, $Sm_{12}Co_{59}Cu_6Fe_{20}Zr_3$ sintered magnets made from as-cast alloy and melt-spun ribbons, Journal of Alloys and Compounds, Volume 486, Issues 1-2, 3 November 2009, Pages 819-823.

18) Ji-bing Sun, Dan Han, Chun-xiang Cui, Wei Yang, Liang Li, Fan Yang, Li-guo Yang, Effects of Hf and CNTs on structure and magnetic properties of $TbCu_7$-type Sm–Co magnets, Intermetallics, Volume 18, Issue 4, April 2010, Pages 599-605.

19) Dong, Tianshun; Cui, Chunxiang; Liu, Shuangjin; Liu, Fucai, Study on the rapid solidification and refining mechanism of Al-Ti-B refiner, Rare Metal Materials and Engineering, v 37, n 1, January, 2008, p 29-32.

20) Zhao, Lichen; Cui, Chunxiang; Liu, Shuangjin; Zhang, Zhe, Design and research on properties of new type metastable -titanium alloys for biomedical applications based on the d-electron alloy design method, Rare Metal Materials and Engineering, v 37, n 1, January, 2008, p 108-111.

21) Cao, D.X.; Zhu, N.H.; Cui, C.X.; Tan, R.H., An agent-based framework for guiding conceptual design of mechanical products, International Journal of Production Research, v 46, n 9, May, 2008, Enabling Technologies and Frameworks for Collaborative Intelligent Manufacturing, p 2381-2396.

22) Sun, Jibing; Wang, Hairong; An, Yaqin; Cui, Chunxiang; Han, Dan Progress on long persistence luminescent materials, Rare Metal Materials and Engineering, v 37, n 2, February, 2008, p 189-194.

23) Tan, B.M. Yuan, J.Y.; Niu, X.H.; Shi, H.L.; Liu, Y.L.; Cui, C.X. Study on CMP slurry and technique of silicon dioxide dielectric for ULSI Key Engineering Materials, v 373-374, 2008, p 798-801.

24) Dong, Tianshun; Cui, Chunxiang; Liu, Shuangjin; Yang, Lijun; Sun, Jibing Influence of rapid solidification of Cu-P intermediate alloy on wear resistance of Al-Si alloy Rare Metal Materials and Engineering, v 37, n 4, April, 2008, p 686-689.

25) Cao, D.X.; Jia, Q.L.; Han, Y.H.; Cui, C.X. Port-based description of functional modeling for product conceptual design Journal of Advanced Manufacturing Systems, v 7, n 1, June, 2008, p 101-105.

26) Wang, Xin; Cui, Chunxiang; Qi, Yumin; Liu, Shuangjin; Huang, Nan; Han, Dan High temperature metastability of potassium tetratitanate whisker Journal of the Chinese Ceramic Society, vol. 36, 2008(6) 829-831+837.

27) Bai, Ling; Cui, Chunxiang; Wang, Qingzhou; Bu, Shaojing; Qi, Yumin,Ti-Zr-Fe-Si system amorphous alloys with excellent biocompatibility, Journal of Non-Crystalline Solids, vol. 354, n 33, 2008(9)3935-3938.

28) Dong, Tianshun; Cui, Chunxiang; Liu, Shuangjin; Yang, Lijun; Sun, Jibing, Influence of rapid solidification of Cu-P intermediate alloy on wear resistance of Al-Si alloy, Rare Metal Materials and Engineering, vol. 37, 2008(4)686-689.

In: Materials Science Researcher Biographical Sketches …   ISBN: 978-1-61942-153-0
Editors: Satomi Matsumoto and Ueda Iwate   © 2013 Nova Science Publishers, Inc.

Chapter 4

BIOGRAPHICAL SKETCH

Qiang Dou, PhD, Associate Professor

Affiliation: College of Materials Science and Engineering, Nanjing University of Technology

Date of Birth: May 2, 1970

Address: No 5, Xinmofan Road, Nanjing, Jiangsu Province, China

Research and Professional Experience

He received an MSc in polymer materials and a PhD in chemical engineering in 1995 and 2008, respectively. He began the teaching career at Nanjing University of Technology in 1995. His research interests focus on thermoplastics composites.

Professional Appointments

Associate Professor

Publications during last three years

Qiang Dou, Ming-rui Meng, Lin Li. Effect of pimelic acid treatment on the crystallization, morphology, and mechanical properties of isotactic polypropylene/mica composites. Polymer Composites, 2010, 31: 1572-1584.

Lin Li, Qiang Dou. Effect of malonic acid treatment on the crystal structure, melting behavior, morphology, and mechanical properties of isotactic poly(propylene)/ wollastonite composites. Polymer Composites, 2010, 31: 966-973.

Qiang Dou. Effect of malonic acid/calcium stearate bicomponent nucleator on the Î²-crystalline formation in isotactic poly(propylene). International Polymer Processing, 2010, XXV(5): 334-340.

Qiang Dou. Effect of N,N'-diphenyl adipamide on the formation of the $\hat{I}^2$-crystalline form in isotactic polypropylene. Journal of Applied Polymer Science 2009, 111: 1738-1744.

Qiang Dou, Jingbo Wang. Study on transparent poly(propylene) nucleated by the "in situ" reaction products of dehydroabietic acid and sodium stearate. Journal of Applied Polymer Science 2009, 111: 2436-2444.

Qiang Dou, Qu-Liang Lu, Huai-Dong Li. Effect of metallic salts of glutaric acid on the formation of $\hat{I}^2$-crystalline form in isotactic polypropylene. Journal of Elastomers and Plastics 2009, 41: 509-522.

Quliang Lu, Qiang Dou. $\hat{I}^2$-crystal formation of isotactic polypropylene induced by N,N'-dicyclohexylsuccinamide. Journal of Polymer Research 2009, 16: 555-560.

Quliang Lu, Qiang Dou. Effect of a novel family of N,N'-diphenyl bisamides on the formation of $\hat{I}^2$ crystalline form in isotactic polypropylene. Polymer Journal 2009, 41: 254-259.

Ming-Rui Meng, Qiang Dou. Effect of filler treatment on crystallization, morphology and mechanical properties of polypropylene/calcium carbonate composites. Journal of Macromolecular Science, Part B: Physics 2009, 48: 213-225.

Jingbo Wang, Qiang Dou. Polypropylene/linear low-density polyethylene blends: morphology, crystal structure, optical, and mechanical properties. Journal of Applied Polymer Science 2009, 111: 194-202.

Qiang Dou. Effect of the composition ratio of pimelic acid/calcium stearate bicomponent nucleator and crystallization temperature on the production of $\hat{I}^2$ crystal form in isotactic polypropylene. Journal of Applied Polymer Science 2008, 107(2): 958-965.

Qiang Dou. A comparison of the effects of calcium glutarate and pimelate on the formation of $\hat{I}^2$ crystalline form in isotactic poly(propylene). Journal of Macromolecular Science, Part B: Physics 2008, 47(1):127-138.

Qiang Dou. Effect of calcium salts of glutaric acid and pimelic acid on the formation of $\hat{I}^2$ crystalline form in isotactic polypropylene. Polymer - Plastics Technology and Engineering 2008, 47(9): 851-857.

Qiang Dou, Qu-liang Lu, Huai-dong Li. Effect of metallic salts of malonic acid on the formation of $\hat{I}^2$ crystalline form in isotactic polypropylene. Journal of Macromolecular Science, Part B: Physics 2008, 47(5): 900-912.

Qiang Dou, Qu-liang Lu. Effect of magnesium malonate on the formation of the $\hat{I}^2$ crystalline form in isotactic polypropylene. Journal of Vinyl and Additive Technology 2008, 14(3): 136-141.

Qiang Dou, Qu-liang Lu. Effect of calcium malonate on the formation of $\hat{I}^2$ crystalline form in isotactic poly(propylene). Polymers for Advanced Technologies 2008, 19: 1522-1527.

Jingbo Wang, Qiang Dou. Crystallization behavior and optical and mechanical properties of isotactic polypropylene nucleated with rosin-based nucleating agents. Polymer International 2008, 57(2):233-239.

Qu-liang Lu, Qiang Dou. Crystalline form transition in isotactic polypropylene with addition of N,N' -diphenyl succinamide. Journal of Macromolecular Science, Part B: Physics 2008, 47(3):463-471.

Jingbo Wang, Qiang Dou, Xianyi Chen, Di Li. Crystal structure and morphologies of polypropylene homopolymer and propylene-ethylene random copolymer: Effect of the substituted 1,3,5-benzenetrisamides. Journal of Polymer Science, Part B: Polymer Physics 2008, 46(11): 1067-1078.

Jingbo Wang, Qiang Dou. Nonisothermal crystallization kinetics and melting behaviors of isotactic polypropylene/N,N',N"-tris- tert.butyl-1,3,5-benzene-tricarboxamide. Journal of Macromolecular Science, Part B: Physics 2008, 47(4): 629-642.

Ming-Rui Meng, Qiang Dou. Effect of pimelic acid on the crystallization, morphology and mechanical properties of polypropylene/wollastonite composites. Materials Science and Engineering A 2008, 492(1-2): 177-184.

Quliang Lu, Qiang Dou. Crystalline form transformation of isotactic polypropylene induced by N,N'-diphenyl glutaramide. e-Polymers 2008, no. 076.

Jingbo Wang, Qiang Dou. Crystallization behaviors and optical properties of isotactic polypropylene: Comparative study of a trisamide and a rosin-type nucleating agent. Colloid and Polymer Science 2008, 286(6-7): 699-705.

In: Materials Science Researcher Biographical Sketches …   ISBN: 978-1-61942-153-0
Editors: Satomi Matsumoto and Ueda Iwate   © 2013 Nova Science Publishers, Inc.

Chapter 5

BIOGRAPHICAL SKETCH

Mohamed Saada El-Deab

Affiliation: Professor of Physical Chemistry

Date of Birth: 1 December 1968

Education

Institution and Location	Degree	Year Conferred	Scientific Field
Faculty of Science, Cairo University	B.Sc. (Distinction with first class honors)	1990	Major Chemistry
"Electrolytic Production of Hydrogen Using Porous Flow-Through Electrodes", Cairo University	M.Sc.	1994	Physical Chemistry
"Electrochemical Removal of Lead Ions Using Porous Flow-Through Electrodes", Cairo University	Ph.D.	1999	Physical Chemistry

Contact Points

Permanent Address:
Department of Chemistry,
Faculty of Science, Cairo University,
Cairo, Egypt.
Tel: +202-3567-6603;

Fax: +202-3572-7556
E-mail addresses: msaada68@yahoo.com

Awards, Honors and Post-Doc Fellowships

(1) JICA Research-fellow, Department of Interfacial Energy Conversion, Catalysis Research Center, Hokkaido University, Sapporo, Japan, (Aug. 1997 – Feb. 1998).

(2) JSPS Post-Doc fellowship, Department of Electronic Chemistry, Interdisciplinary Graduate School of Science and Engineering, Tokyo Institute of Technology (TIT), Yokohama, Japan, (Sep. 2001 – Sep. 2003).

(3) Post-Doc fellow, Matsushita Electric Corporation in collaboration with Tokyo Institute of Technology (TIT), Yokohama, Japan, (Dec., 2003 – March 2005).

(4) NEDO Post-Doc fellow, Department of Electronic Chemistry, Interdisciplinary Graduate School of Science and Engineering, Tokyo Institute of Technology (TIT), Yokohama, Japan, (Jun. 2005 – Mar. 2007).

(5) JSPS Visiting Professor, Department of Electronic Chemistry, Interdisciplinary Graduate School of Science and Engineering, Tokyo Institute of Technology (TIT), Yokohama, Japan, (April 2007 – Dec. 2007).

(6) Alexander von Humboldt fellowship, Institute of Electrochemistry, Ulm University, 89069 Ulm, Germany, (Jan. 2008 – Nov. 2009).

Appointments and Employment record

- Instructor, Department of Chemistry, Faculty of Science, Cairo University, Dec. 1990 – Aug. 1994.
- Teaching Assistant, Department of Chemistry, Faculty of Science, Cairo University, Sep. 1994- Nov. 1999.
- Lecturer of Physical Chemistry, Department of Chemistry, Faculty of Science, Cairo University, Dec. 1999 – March 2005.
- Associate Professor, Department of Chemistry, Faculty of Science, Cairo University, April 2005 – Aug. 2010.
- Professor of Physical Chemistry, Department of Chemistry, Faculty of Science, Cairo University, Sep. 2010 – to date.

Memberships

1- Member of the Electrochemical Society (ECS), USA.
2- Member of the International Society of Electrochemistry (ISE), Switzerland.
3- Member of the Electrochemical Society of Japan (ECSJ).
4- Member of the Egyptian Electrochemical Society (EECS), Cairo, Egypt.
5- Active Member of the continuous Chemistry-teaching Program sponsored by the Egyptian Syndicate of Scientific Professions and Cairo University, Egypt.

Research Experiences

1- Fabrication, characterization of metal and metal oxide nanostructures (e.g., Au, TaOx, and MnOx) with tunable size, geometry and crystallographic orientation for electrocatalytic processes in energy conversion systems e.g., oxygen reduction reaction, water electrolysis (oxygen and hydrogen evolution reactions) as well as formic acid oxidation.

2- Functionalization of bulk and nano-structured Au electrodes via the formation of molecular-level phase separated self-assembled monolayer of mono, bi or ternary thiol species and their use as sensors of biologically active species and electrochemical conversion of nitrate ions into ammonia.

3- Electrochemical applications of modified porous flow-through electrodes in water electrolysis (electrolytic production of hydrogen gas) and in wastewater treatment (removal of heavy metal ions from wastewater streams).

4- Studies on the integrity of metallic structures (mainly steels) under the influence of aggressive media and the prevention of its breakdown (corrosion) using blends of different organic and/or non organic inhibitors.

Scientific Supervision

1- *In Egypt:* Acting as a supervisor for two M. Sc. Students who were graduated from Cairo University in 2003, in the fields of (i) enhanced water electrolysis towards the efficient electrogeneration of high purity hydrogen gas and (ii) corrosion prevention and control of metallic structures using eco-friendly corrosion inhibitors. Currently, acting as a supervisor for two Ph.D. students in Cairo University and Mubarak City of Science and Technology.

2- *In Japan:* Acting as a co-supervisor for 5 M.Sc. and 3 Ph.D. students (co-supervised with Professor Takeo Ohsaka, Tokyo Institute of Technology) who were graduate from Department of Electronic Chemistry, Tokyo Institute of Technology, Japan during the period from 2001-2008 in the field of catalysis and electrocatalysis at nanoparticles-based electrodes.

Reviewing Activity

Acting as a reviewer for the following International Journals:
(1) Electrochimica Acta,
(2) Journal of Electroanalytical Chemistry,
(3) Electrochemistry Communications,
(4) International Journal of Hydrogen Energy,
(5) International J. Electrochemical Science
(6) Talanta.

Teaching Experience

1- Teaching of experimental Physical Chemistry classes along with several Computer-assisted Chemistry courses for the undergraduate students at Chemistry Department, Cairo University.

2- Teaching of several Physical Chemistry courses for freshmen and B.Sc. students at the Chemistry Department, Faculty of Science, Cairo University (e.g., Surface Chemistry, Chemical Thermodynamics, General Chemistry, Introduction to Electrocatalysis, Chemical Kinetics, Electrochemistry of Reversible and Irreversible Systems) for the undergraduate and the B.Sc. students at Chemistry Department, Cairo University.

List of Publications

2010

1- *"Hydrogen spillover phenomenon: Enhanced reversible hydrogen adsorption/desorption at Ta_2O_5-coated Pt electrode in acidic media"*, S. Sata, M. I. Awad, **M. S. El-Deab**, T. Okajima and T. Ohsaka, *Electrochim. Acta* 55 (2010) 3528.

2- *"Electrocatalysis by Nanoparticles: Oxidation of formic acid at manganese oxide nanorods-modified Pt planar and nanohole arrays"*, **M. S. El-Deab**, *J. Adv. Research* 1 (2010) 87-93.

3- *"Effects of electrolyte viscosity on the efficiency of the electrochemical removal of lead ions using porous flow-through electrodes"* **M. S. El-Deab**, M. M. Saleh, B. E. El-Anadouli and B. G. Ateya, *Egyptian J. Chem.*, (2010) in press.

2009

4- *"On the preferential crystallographic orientation of Au nanoparticles: Effect of electrodeposition time"*, **M. S. El-Deab**, *Electrochim. Acta* 54 (2009) 3720-3725.

5- *"Enhanced electro-oxidation of formic acid at manganese oxide single crystalline nanorod-modified Pt electrodes"*, **M. S. El-Deab**, L. A. Kibler and D. M. Kolb, *Electrochem. Commun.* 11 (2009) 776-778.

6- *"Novel procedure for the fabrication of gold nanostructures enriched in Au (110) facet orientation"*, S. H. Othman, **M. S. El-Deab**, T. Okajima and T. Ohsaka, *Electrochem. Commun.* 11 (2009) 776-778.

7- *"Electrocatalytic oxidation of methanol at γ-MnOOH nanorods modified Pt electrodes"*, **M. S. El-Deab**, *Int. J. Electrochem. Sci.* 4 (2009) 1329-1338.

2008

8- *"Bisthiol-Assisted Multilayers' Self-Assembly of Gold Nanoparticles: Synthesis, Characterization, Size Control, and Electrocatalytic Applications"*, A. I.

Abdelrahman, A. M. Mohammad, **M. S. El-Deab**, T. Okajima and T. Ohsaka, *Macromol. Symp.*, 270 (2008) 74-81.

9- *"Non-platinum electrocatalysts: Manganese oxide nanoparticles-cobaltporphyrin binary catalysts for oxygen reduction" "*, **M. S. El-Deab,** S. H. Othman, T. Okajima and T. Ohsaka, *J. Appl. Electrochem.* 38 (2008) 1445-1451.

10- *"Electrocatalysis by Nanoparticles: Optimization of the Loading Level and Operating pH for the Oxygen Evolution at Crystallographically Oriented Manganese Oxide Nanorods Modified Electrodes"*, A. M. Mohammad, M. I. Awad, **M. S. El-Deab**, T. Okajima and T. Ohsaka, *Electrochim Acta* 53 (13) (2008) 4351-4358.

11- *"On the aggregation phenomena of Au nanoparticles: Effect of substrate roughness on the particle size"*, A. M. Mohammad, A. I. Abdelrahman, **M. S. El-Deab**, T. Okajima and T. Ohsaka, *Coll. Surf. A: Physicochem. Eng. Aspects* 318 (1-3) (2008) 78-83.

12- *"Electrosynthesis of Single-Crystalline MnOOH Nanorods onto Pt Electrodes: Electrocatalytic activity towards Reduction of Oxygen"*, **M. S. El-Deab** and T. Ohsaka, *J. Electrochem. Soc.*, 155 (1) (2008) D14-D21.

In: Materials Science Researcher Biographical Sketches …   ISBN: 978-1-61942-153-0
Editors: Satomi Matsumoto and Ueda Iwate   © 2013 Nova Science Publishers, Inc.

Chapter 6

BIOGRAPHICAL SKETCH

Yurii Fridman, Professor

Date of Birth: 8th of December, 1957

Education

Institution and Location	Degree	Year Conferred	Scientific Field
Chair of theoretical physics, Physics department of M.V. Frunze Simferopol state university, Simferopol, Ukraine			

Contact Points: frid@tnu.crimea.ua

Research and Professional Experience

More than 25 years of scientific studies in the areas of magnetism, magnetic phase transitions, magnetoelastic properties, dynamics of the magnetic systems.

Professional Appointments

Professor, Head of the Chair of theoretical physics in V.I. Vernadsky Taurida national university

Publications Last 3 Years

1) Yu.A. Fridman, O.A. Kosmachev, Ph.N. Klevets. "Phase states of S = 1 magnetic with anisotropic exchange interactions" // Journal of Magnetism and Magnetic Materials. – 2008. – Vol. 320. – P. 435-449.

2) Yu.A. Fridman, Ph.N. Klevets, A.P. Voytenko. "Phase diagram of $Fe_{1-x}Co_x$ ultrathin film" // Journal of Magnetism and Magnetic Materials. – 2008. – Vol. 320. – P. 3370-3377.

3) Yu.A. Fridman, D.A. Matunin, O.A. Kosmachev, Ph.N. Klevets. "Influence of magnetic dipole and magnetoelastic interactions on the phase states of 2D non-Heisenberg ferromagnetic with complex exchange interactions" // Journal of Magnetism and Magnetic Materials. – 2009. – Vol. 321. – P. 3782-3794.

4) Yu.A. Fridman, O.A. Kosmachev, D.A. Matunin, G.A. Gorelikov, Ph.N. Klevets. "Influence of strong single-ion anisotropy on phase states of 3D and 2D frustrated magnets" // Journal of Magnetism and Magnetic Materials. – 2010. – Vol. 322. – P. 3196-3203.

In: Materials Science Researcher Biographical Sketches ...   ISBN: 978-1-61942-153-0

Editors: Satomi Matsumoto and Ueda Iwate   © 2013 Nova Science Publishers, Inc.

Chapter 7

BIOGRAPHICAL SKETCH

Juan A. Gallego-Juárez

Academic degrees

Doctor Honoris Causa, University of Santiago de Chile, 2004
Doctor Physical Sciences, University of Madrid, 1971
Doctor Physics, University of Rome, Italy, 1970
Master Physical Sciences, University of Madrid, June 1966

Positions held

1991-2003: Director, Institute of Acoustics CSIC
1994-2002: Director, Center for Physical Technologies, CSIC
1971-95 :Head of the Ultrasonics Laboratory of the Institute of Acoustics, CSIC
1988- : Research Professor, CSIC
1973-88: Scientific Researcher, CSIC
1971-72: Scientific Collaborator, CSIC
1969-1970: Scientific Collaborator, CNR
1966-70: Postgraduate Fellow, CSIC and CNR
1965-1966: Graduate Fellow, CSIC

CSIC: National Research Council of Spain
CNR: National Research Council of Italy

Other Professional Activities

- President of the 19th International Congress on Acoustics (ICA2007 MADRID)
- Member of the Boards:
  - International Commission for Acoustics (1998-2007)
  - International Congress on Ultrasonics

- o   Spansih Acoustical Society
- Fellow
  - o   Acoustical Society of America
  - o   British Institute of Acoustics
- Member
  - o   New York Academy of Sciences
  - o   IEEE
  - o   Ultrasonic Industry Association
- Chairman of the Technical Committee on Ultrasound of the European Acoustical Association (2002-2007)

Awards

- Gold medal of the University of Santiago de Chile, 2004
- Honor Diploma of the Portuguese Acoustical Society (2004)
- Backok Foundation Prize to Technological Innovation, 1995
- Saving Bank of Cordoba Prize to Scientific Research, (Ph.D. Thesis) 1971

Contribution to Ultrasonics

His research work has always been related to ultrasonics, particularly high-power ultrasonics, transducers and applications.

He is the author of more than 200 publications and holds 38 patents.

His major contribution to Acoustics is in the field of **High-Power Ultrasound** and more specially in the study, design, development and characterization of **new power sonic and ultrasonic generators**, in their application to the production of **macrosonic processes** and in the study of the corresponding **nonlinear phenomena** involved in such processes.

The first achievement to be pointed out is the invention and development of a **new type of power sonic and ultrasonic transducer for use in gases and multiphase media** (gas-liquid, gas-solid): the stepped-plate transducer. This transducer mainly consists of a large plate radiator of stepped profile which is driven by a piezoelectric or magnetostrictive vibrator. The stepped plate radiator is vibrating in one of its flexural modes and is tuned with a piezoelectric extensional vibrator. The new transducers are characterized by the efficient generation of high-directional (coherent) and/or focusing radiation.

Among the several **macrosonic applications** he has studied and developed, the following have to be mentioned: aerosol agglomeration, defoaming, dehydration, textile washing, debubbling and supercritical fluids extraction assisted by ultrasound.

The application of sonic and ultrasonic energy for **particle agglomeration and precipitation** is to be applied in problems such as cleaning of smoke, powder precipitation in mines, precipitation of toxic clouds, etc.

Ultrasonic defoaming is basically pointed towards food and beverage industries where chemical anti-foam agents may adversely affect the product. Several systems have been developed and successfully applied in various industrial problems.

Dehydration is a process in which the liquid is removed from a product without changing its phase. By using high power ultrasound a process is developed to realease moisture. Such a process has been applied for food drying as well as for post filtration dewatering of sludges.

Washing of textiles by using ultrasound is a process which offers more problems than cleaning of rigid materials. Nevertheless, a new ultrasonic washing process has been implemented based on the production of cavitation in a thin layer of liquid. A pilot ultrasonic washing machine working in continous has been developed. This process is useful in textile manufacture and other industrial applications.

Debubbling is other important technological tasks in which he was involved in the research and development of the application of ultrasonic energy for superficial homogeneisation of industrial coating.

The application of **ultrasonic energy to accelerate supercritical fluid extraction processes** represents a new way to improve a technique which is emergent in food industry.

The majority of these new ultrasonic processes have been patented and to exploit such an important potential, Prof. Gallego-Juárez promoted in 2008 the creation of the Spin-off Company PUSONICS, S.L.

In the investigation of **nonlinear phenomena** his contribution can be summarized in the following studies: propagation of finite amplitude (spherical and plane) ultrasonic waves in air, finite amplitude longitudinal and flexural standing waves at ultrasonic frequencies in metallic bars, nonlinear effects in multiphase media and transient (inertial) cavitation in gassy liquids. Among the various achievements the following are to be mentioned: experimental study of all the propagation regions of finite-amplitude waves and verification at ultrasonic frequencies of some theoretical models (weak shock theory for spherical waves and Rudnick model for plane waves); development of theoretical models for finite-amplitude standing waves and experimental verification; development of a method for the determination of the nonlinearity parameter of solid materials; development procedure to determine the ultrasonic fatigue limit of metallic materials, development of a semiempirical model for acoustic agglomeration of aerosol particles; and finally the detection of two different types of transient cavitation in a gassy liquid and the establishment of a new method to detect the inception of transient (inertial) cavitation.

In: Materials Science Researcher Biographical Sketches ...   ISBN: 978-1-61942-153-0
Editors: Satomi Matsumoto and Ueda Iwate   © 2013 Nova Science Publishers, Inc.

Chapter 8

BIOGRAPHICAL SKETCH

Hae Kyung Jeong, Prof. Dr

Date of Birth: July 02, 1970

Education

Institution and Location	Degree	Year Conferred	Scientific Field
University of Nebraska-Lincoln	PhD.	2003	Physics
POSTECH, Korea	MS.	1996	Physics
ChonBuk National University	BS.	1992	Physics

Research and Professional Experience

- 1996-1998, Researcher, LG Electronics, Korea
- 2004, Postdoctoral research associate at University of Nebraska-Lincoln
- 2005-2006, Postdoctoral research associate at Brookhaven National Laboratory
- 2006-2009, Research Professor at Sungkyunkwan University, Korea
- 2010-present, Professor, Department of Physics, Daegu University, Korea

Research interests

Professional Appointments

- Professor since March, 2010 at Daegu University

Publications during Last Three Years

Lingmei Kong, Cameron Bjelkevig, Sneha Gaddam, Mi Zhou, Young Hee Lee, Gang Hee Han, **Hae Kyung Jeong**, Ning Wu, Zhengzheng Zhang, Jie Xiao, P. A. Dowben, Jeffry

A. Kelber, "Graphene/substrate charge transfer characterization by inverse photoelectron spectroscopy", Â accepted to The Journal of Physical Chemistry C.

Gang Hee Han, SeungJin Chae, Eun Sung Kim, Fethullah G u nes, Il Ha Lee, **Hae Kyung Jeong**, and Young Hee Lee, "Laser etching and nanoribbon formation of graphene"• Â accepted to ACSNano.

Hae Kyung Jeong, ki-jeong Kim, Soo Min Kim, Young Hee Lee, " Modification of the Electronic Structures of Graphene by Viologen", *Chemical Physics Letters* 498 (2010) 168-171.

Hae Kyung Jeong, C. Yang, B. S. Kim, K.-j. Kim, "Valence Band of Graphite Oxide", EPL 92 (2010) 37005.

Eun Ju Ra, Jung Jun Bae, Tae Hyung Kim, Woo Jong Yu, **Hae-Kyung Jeong**, Kay Hyeok An, Young Hee Lee, "Immobilization of Pt Nanoparticles on Hydrolyzed Polyacrylonitrile-Based Nanofiber Paper", submitted to *The Journal of Physical Chemistry.*

Meihua Jin, **Hae-Kyung Jeong,** Tae-Hyung Kim, Kang Pyo So, Yan Cui, Woo Jong Yu, Eun Ju Ra, Young Hee Lee, " Synthesis and systematic characterization of functionalized graphene sheets by thermal exfoliation at low temperature"• , *Journal of Physics D:Applied Physics* 43 (2010) 275402 (7pp).

Hae-Kyung Jeong, Meihua Jin, Eun Ju Ra, Kyu Yun Sim, Young Hee Lee, " Enhanced Electric Double Layer Capacitance of Graphite Oxide Intercalated by Poly(Sodium 4-Styrensulfonate) with High Cycle Stability"• , ACS Nano 4 (2010) 1162. Il Ha Lee, Gang Hee Han, Seung Jin Chae, Jung Jun Bae, Eun Sung Kim, Su Min Kim, Tae Hyung Kim, **Hae-Kyung Jeong,** and Young Hee Lee, " Yarning Criteria from Vertically Aligned Carbo n Nanotubes", *Nano* 5 (2010) 31.

Hong-Zhang Geng, Tae Hyung Kim, Seong Ghu Lim, **Hae-Kyung Jeong,** Mei Hua Jin, Young Woo Jo, and Young Hee Lee, " Hydrogen storage in microwave-treated multi-walled carbon nanotubes"• International Journal of Hydrogen Energy 35 (2010) 2073-2082.

Dinh Loc Dung, Gunn Kim, **Hae-Kyung Jeong,** and Young Hee Lee, " Breaking AB stacking order in graphite oxide: ab initio approach", *Physical Chemistry Chemical Physics* 12, 7, (2010) 1595-1599, Royal Society of Chemistry. **Hae-Kyung Jeong,** Mei Hua Jin, Kay Hyeok An, and Young Hee Lee, "Structural Stability and Variable Dielectric Constant in Poly Sodium 4-Styrensulfonate Intercalated Graphite Oxide"• , *The Journal of Physical Chemistry C* 113 (30) 2009, 13060-13064 (07/30/2009) ACS Publications

Hae-Kyung Jeong, Meihua Jin, Woo Jong Yu, Dong Jae Bae, Bo Ram Kang and Young Hee Lee, "Graphene oxide thin film field effect transistors without reduction"• , *Journal of Physics D:Applied Physics* 42 (2009) 135109 (5pp) (06/19/2009) IOP Publishing Hyeon-Jin Shin, Ki Kang Kim, Anass Benayad, Seon-Mi Yoon, Hyeon Ki Park, In-Sun Jung, Mei Hua Jin, **Hae-Kyung Jeong,** Jong Min Kim, Jae-Young Choi, and Young Hee Lee, "Efficient Reduction of Graphite Oxide by Sodium Borohydride and Its Effect on Electrical Conductance"• , *Advanced Functional Materials* 19 (2) (2009) 1987-1992 (06/23/2009) Wiley-VCH InterScience

Anass Benayad, Hyeon-Jin Shin, Hyeon Ki Park, Seon-Mi Yoon, Ki Kang Kim, Mei Hua Jin, **Hae-Kyung Jeong,** Jae Cheol Lee, Jae-Young Choi, and Young Hee Lee, "Controlling Work Function of Reduced Graphite Oxide with Au-Ion Concentration", *Chemical*

Physics Letters 475 (2009) 91-95 (online05/14/2009, published 06/16/2009) Elsevier Takashi Komesu, **H. K. Jeong,** David Wooten, Ya. B. Losovyj, J. N. Crain, M. Bissen, F. J. Himpsel, J. Petrosky, Jinke Tang, Wendong Wang, I. N. Yakovkin, and P. A. Dowben, "4f hybridization and band dispersion in gadolinium thin films and compounds"• , *Physica Status Solidi (b)* 246 (2009) 975-980 (04/03/2009) Wiley-VCH Interscience

Fethullah G u ne ?, Gang Hee Han, Ki Kang Kim, Eun Sung Kim, Seung Jin Chae, Min Ho Park, **Hae-Kyung Jeong,** Seong Chu Lim and Young Hee Lee, "Large-Area Graphene-Based Flexible Transparent Conducting Films", Nano: Brief Reports and Reviews 4, No. 2 (2009) 83-90 (04//2009) World Scientific Publishing R.J.W.E. Lahaye, **Hae-Kyung Jeong,** C. Y. Park, and Young Hee Lee, "Density functional theory study of graphite oxide for different oxidation levels", *Physical Review B* 79 (2009) 125435 (03/27/2009), APS

Hae-Kyung Jeong, Han-Jin Noh, Jae-Young Kim, Leyla Colakerol, Per-Anders Glans, Mei Hua Jin, Kevin E. Smith, and Young Hee Lee, "Comment on Near-Edge X-ray Absorption Fine-Structure Investigation of Graphene", *Physical Review Letters 102 (2009) 099701* (03/06/2009) APS **Hae-Kyung Jeong,** Yun Pyo Lee, Mei Hua Jin, Eun Sung Kim, Jung Jun Bae, and Young Hee Lee, "Thermal stability of graphite oxide", *Chemical Physics Letters* 470(2009)255-258, (03/05/2009) Elsevier

Hae-Kyung Jeong, Mei Hua Jin, K. P. So, S. C. Lim and Y. H. Lee, "Tailoring characteristics of graphite oxides by different oxidation times"• , *Journal of Physics D: Applied Physics* 42(2009)065418, (03/03/2009) IOP Publishing Nguyen Thi Xuyen, **Hae Kyung Jeong,** Gunn Kim, Kang Pyo So, Kay Heyok An, and Young Hee Lee, "Hydrolysis-induced immobilization of Pt(acac)2 on polyimide nanofiber mat in the formation of Pt nanoparticles", *Journal of Materials Chemistry* 19 (2009) 1283-1288 (online 01/26/2009) The Royal Society of Chemistry

Hae-Kyung Jeong, Leyla Colakerol, Mei Hua Jin, Per-Anders Glans, Kevin E. Smith, and Young Hee Lee, "Unoccupied electronics states in graphite oxides", *Chemical Physics Letters* 460 (2008) 499-502 (07/30/2008), Elsevier **Hae-Kyung Jeong,** Han-Jin Noh, Jae-Yeong Kim, Mei Hua Jin, Chong Yun Park, and Young Hee Lee, "X-ray absorption spectroscopy study of graphite oxide"• *EPL* 82 (2008) 67004(p1-p5), (06/04/2008), EDP

Hae-Kyung Jeong, Yun Pyo Lee, Rob J. W. E. Lahaye, Min-Ho Park, Kay Hyeok An, Ick Jun Kim, Cheol-Woong Yang, Chong Yun Park, Rodney S. Ruoff, Young Hee Lee, "Evidence of Graphitic AB Stacking Order of Graphite Oxides", *Journal of the American Chemical Society* 130 (4) (2008) 1362-1366 (01/30/2008), ACS publications

In: Materials Science Researcher Biographical Sketches …   ISBN: 978-1-61942-153-0
Editors: Satomi Matsumoto and Ueda Iwate   © 2013 Nova Science Publishers, Inc.

Chapter 9

BIOGRAPHICAL SKETCH

Jing Li, Ph. D.

Date of Birth: 12/02/1976

Education

Institution and Location	Degree	Year Conferred	Scientific Field
Institute of Metal Research, Chinese Academy of Sciences			

Address: Wenhua Road 72, Shenyang 110016, China

Research and Professional Experience

6 years on hydrogen storage in zeolites

Professional Appointments

Research associate at IMR

Publications during last three years

About 3 research papers and 2 reviewe papers

In: Materials Science Researcher Biographical Sketches …   ISBN: 978-1-61942-153-0

Editors: Satomi Matsumoto and Ueda Iwate   © 2013 Nova Science Publishers, Inc.

Chapter 10

BIOGRAPHICAL SKETCH

Dr. Daqing Liu

Date of Birth: Jul. 1st, 1971

Education

Institution and Location	Degree	Year Conferred	Scientific Field
Institute of High Energy Physics, Chinese Academy of Science, Concentrations: Lattice Gauge Theory, Quantum Chromodynamics (QCD), Guleballs in QCD;	Ph.D.	2001	Theoretical Physics
National University of Defense Technology, China, Concentrations: Particle Simulations, Inertial Confinement fusion, Laser-plasma Interactions	M.A.	1996	Applied Physics
National University of Defense Technology, China, Concentrations: Microwave Engineering, Electronic Engineering, Antenna.	B.A.	1993	Electronic Technique

Contact Points

Department of Applied Physics, School of Science,
Xi'an Jiaotong University, No. 28, Xianning West Road, Xi'an, 710049, China

Research and Professional Experience

1) 2006-present, Staff in School of Science, Xi'an Jiaotong University, Concentrations: Condensed Matter Physics, Theoretical Physics, Graphene.

2) 2003-2005, Postdoctor in Institute of High Energy Physics, Chinese Academy of Science. Concentrations: Lattice gauge Theory, Quantum chromodynamics, Glueball in QCD.

3) 2001-2003, Postdoctor in Institute of Theoretical Physics, Chinese Academy of Science. Concentrations: Lattice gauge theory, Quantum chromodynamics, Charmonium spectrum.

4) 1996-1998, Staff in China's Ministry of Aeronautics and Astronautics, Responsibilities: Measurement and control of satellite.

Publications during last three years

1) Daqing Liu, Xinghua Liu, Yanshen Wang, General Form of the SpecialTheory of Relativity, Physics Essays, revised.

2) Daqing LIU, Shengli ZHANG, Erhu ZHANG, Ning MA, Huawei CHEN, Anomalous valley magnetic moment of graphene, Europhysics Letters 89, 37002 (2010).

3) Daqing LIU, On Wave Functional in QED, Canadian Journal of Physics, 87(6) 729-733 (2009).

4) Da-Qing LIU and Sheng-Li ZHANG, Kramers-Kronig Relation of Grapheme Conductivity, J. Phys.: Cond.Matter, 20, 271553(2008)

5) LIU Da-Qing, Quantum Study of Foldy-Wouthuysen-Tani Theory on Lattice, Chinese Physics, V16, 1009(2007).

6) LIU Da-Qing, Compute the Real Orthogonal Form of [n-1,1] Representation of Sn Group in a Special Representation Space, High Energy Physics and Nuclear Physics, V31 1099(2007).

In: Materials Science Researcher Biographical Sketches …　　ISBN: 978-1-61942-153-0

Editors: Satomi Matsumoto and Ueda Iwate　　© 2013 Nova Science Publishers, Inc.

Chapter 11

BIOGRAPHICAL SKETCH

Luca Magagnin

Affiliation: Professor, PhD in Electrochemical Engineering

Date of Birth: September 26th, 1970

Contact Points: luca.magagnin@polimi.it

Research and Professional Experience

Electrochemistry, plating, corrosion, MEMS

Professional Appointments

Professor of Surface Engineering and Materials for Electronics - Politecnico di Milano

Honors

January 2011 - Vicepresident IUSF International Union of Surface Finishing

Hans-Jürgen Engell Prize 2003 to younger electrochemists on the basis of published work in the field of corrosion, electrodeposition or surface treatment.

NACE <?xml:namespace prefix = st1 ns = "urn:schemas-microsoft-com:office:smarttags" />2003 A.B. Campbell Award for the most outstanding manuscript published in Corrosion or MP in the previous year by young authors.

Publications during last three years

1)　A. M. Cantaragiu, P. Cojocaru, G. Carac, C. Gheorghies, L. Magagnin, *Electrocodeposition of Ag/TiO2 nanocomposite coatings in cyanide free electrolytes*, Transactions of the Institute of Metals Finishing, in press (2010).

2) W. Navarrini, T. Brivio, D. Capobianco, M.V. Diamanti, M. Pedeferri, L. Magagnin, Giuseppe Resnati, *Anti-fingerprints fluorinated coating for anodized titanium avoiding color alteration*, J. Coat. Technol. Res., in press (2010).

3) P. Cojocaru, L. Magagnin, E. Gomez, E. Valles, F. Liu, C. Carraro, R. Maboudian, *Magnetic micromechanical structures based on CoNi electrodeposited alloys*, J. Micromech. Microeng. 20 (2010) 125017 (6pp).

4) M. Sansotera, W. Navarrini, L. Magagnin, C.L. Bianchi, A. Sanguineti, P. Metrangolo, G. Resnati, *Hydrophobic carbonaceous materials obtained by covalent bonding of perfluorocarbon and perfluoropolyether chains*, Journal of Materials Chemistry 20 (2010) p. 8607-8616.

5) P. Cojocaru, F. Muscolino, L. Magagnin, *Effect of organic additives on copper dissolution for e-CMP*, Microelectronic Engineering 87, 11 (2010): p. 2187-2189.

6) P. Cojocaru, M. Spreafico, E. Gomez, E. Vallés, L. Magagnin, *Electrocodeposition of CoNi/barium ferrite using a forced flow cell*, Surface and Coatings Technology 205 (2010) p. 195-199.

7) P. Cojocaru, L. Magagnin, E. Gómez, E. Vallés, *Electrodeposition of CoNi and CoNiP alloys in sulfamate electrolytes*, Journal of Alloys and Compounds 503 (2010) p. 454–459.

8) A. M. Cantaragiu, P. Cojocaru, L. Magagnin, G. Cârâc, C. Gheorghieþ, *Electrophoretic synthesis and characterization of bioactive HAp/TiO2 thin films coated on stainless steel*, Journal of Optoelectronics and Advanced Materials, 12, 4 (2010): p. 913 – 918.

9) L. Magagnin, P. Cojocaru, D. Dietrich, T. Lampke, *Synthesis of nickel-carbon nanohorn composite films by an electrodeposition technique*, ECS Transactions (2010), 25(24, Nanotechnology (General)--216th ECS Meeting, 2009): p. 51-56.

10) P. Cojocaru, F. Muscolino, L. Magagnin, M. Vazquez, G. Badini-Confalonier, G. Carac, *Electrodeposition of Ni/Co and Ni magnetic nanowires using alumina template*, ECS Transactions (2010), 25(27, Semiconductors, Metal Oxides, and Composites: Metallization and Electrodeposition of Thin Films and Nanostructures): p. 147-153.

11) W. Navarrini, C.L. Bianchi, L. Magagnin, L. Nobili, G. Carignano, P. Metrangolo, G. Resnati, M. Sansotera, *Low surface energy coatings covalently bonded on diamond-like carbon films*, Diamond and Related Materials 19(4) (2010) p. 336-341.

12) L. Magagnin, P. Cojocaru, F. Muscolino, P.L. Cavallotti, *Sintesi di compositi di nichel con materiali micro/nano strutturati a base di carbonio per elettrodeposizione*, Galvanotecnica e Nuove Finiture, 5 (2009) p. 290-294.

13) G. Carac, T. Lampke, M. Spreafico, P. Cojocaru, L. Magagnin, *Co-deposition of cerium oxide with nickel and cobalt: correlation between microstructure and microhardness*, Galvanotecnica e Nuove Finiture 19(4) (2009) p. 217-220.

14) A. Cojocaru, S. Costovici, L. Anicai, T. Visan, P. Cojocaru, L. Magagnin, P.L. Cavallotti, *Nickel-tin alloy deposition from choline chloride-urea ionic liquids*, Galvanotecnica e Nuove Finiture 19(3) (2009) p. 140-146.

15) P. Cojocaru, F. Muscolino, L. Magagnin, P.L. Cavallotti, *Electrodeposition of gold composite with carbon nanotubes*, Galvanotecnica e Nuove Finiture 19(2) (2009) p. 88-90.

16) L. Nobili, L. Magagnin, *DLC coatings for hydraulic applications*, Trans. Nonferrous Met. Soc. China 19 (2009): p. 810-813.

17)   A. Benedetti, L. Magagnin, F. Passaretti, E. Chelossi, M. Faimali, G. Montesperelli, *Cathodic protection of carbon steel in natural seawater: Effect of sunlight radiation*, Electrochimica Acta 54 (2009): p. 6472–6478.

18)   E. Pompei, L. Magagnin, N. Lecis, P.L. Cavallotti, *Electrodeposition of nickel–BN composite coatings*, Electrochimica Acta, 54, 9 (2009): p. 2571-2574.

19)   P. Cojocaru, L. Magagnin, L. Nobili, *Rivestimenti DLC per applicazioni anti-usura*, Trattamenti e finiture, 6 (2008): p. 60-65.

20)   L. Magagnin, L. Nobili, *Rivestimenti DLC per applicazioni idrauliche*, Galvanotecnica e Nuove Finiture, 3 (2008): p. 152-154.

21)   S. Galleani, A. Sanvito, F. Pagano, R. Pagano, L. Magagnin, *Funzionalizzazione di superfici di nichel e leghe con monostrati autoassemblati*, Galvanotecnica e Nuove Finiture, 3 (2008): p. 146-150.

22)   P. Cojocaru, A. Vicenzo, L. Magagnin, A.C. West, P.L. Cavallotti, *Electropolishing of copper in presence of benzotriazole,* Galvanotecnica e Nuove Finiture, 1 (2008): p. 20-23.

In: Materials Science Researcher Biographical Sketches …   ISBN: 978-1-61942-153-0
Editors: Satomi Matsumoto and Ueda Iwate   © 2013 Nova Science Publishers, Inc.

Chapter 12

BIOGRAPHICAL SKETCH

Joydeep Maity, Dr., Associate Professor

Date of Birth: 05/12/1973

Education

Institution and Location	Degree	Year Conferred	Scientific Field
BE (Met. Engg)			
ME (Met. Engg.),			
Ph.D. (Engg.)			

Contact Points

Department of Metallurgical and Materials Engineering,
National Institute of Technology Durgapur,
Durgapur – 713209, West Bengal, INDIA.
E-mail: joydeep_maity@yahoo.co.in
Mobile: + 91-9474777821
Phone: +91-343-2754733 (Office)

Research and Professional Experience

More than ten years teaching and research experience in the field of Diffusion, Phase Transformation, Heat treatment, TLP bonding and Metal Matrix Composites.

Professional Appointments

Designation	Organisation	Duration
Project Assistant	Jadavpur university, Kolkata-700032 (Metallurgical Engineering Department)	16/09/1996 to 26/08/1997

Designation	Organisation	Duration
Lecturer	National Institute of Foundry and Forge Technology, Hatia, Ranchi – 834003, India (Materials and Metallurgical Engineering Department)	01/03/2000 to 08/05/2006
Lecturer (Senior Scale)	National Institute of Foundry and Forge Technology, Hatia, Ranchi – 834003, India. (Department of Materials and Metallurgical Engineering)	09/05/2006 to 31/05/2007
Assistant Professor	National Institute of Technology Durgapur, Durgapur – 834003, West Bengal, INDIA (Department of Metallurgical and Materials Engineering)	01/06/2007 to 31/05/2010
Associate professor	National Institute of Technology Durgapur, Durgapur – 834003, West Bengal, INDIA (Department of Metallurgical and Materials Engineering)	01/06/2010 onwards

Honors

Gold Medal (Jadavpur University, 1999), Reviewer of Journal of Materials Engineering and Performance, ASM international, USA.

Publications in last 3 years

1) "A Mathematical Model to Predict Microstructure of Heat-Treated Steel", V. K. Sinha, R. S. Prasad, A. Mandal and J. Maity, Journal of Materials Engineering and Performance, ASM international, USA, August, 2007, Vol. 16, No.4, pp 461-469 (DOI: 10.1007/s11665-007-9041-3).

2) "Microstructural Characterization of TLPD bonded 6061-SiCp Composite": Joydeep Maity, Tapan K. Pal, and Rabindranath Maiti, Journal of Materials Engineering and Performance, ASM international, Vol. 17, No. 5, October, 2008, pp 746-754 (DOI: 10.1007/s11665-008-9211-y).

3) "Microstructural Evaluation and Ultrasonic Characterization of TLPD bonded 6061-SiCp Composite": Joydeep Maity, Tapan Kumar Pal, and Rabindranath Maiti, ISIJ international, Vol. 48, No. 5, May, 2008, pp 616-623.

4) "Transient Liquid Phase Diffusion Bonding of 6061-15 wt% SiCp in Argon Environment": J. Maity, T.K. Pal, and R. Maiti, Journal of Materials Processing Technology, Elsevier, Vol. 209, No.7, April, 2009, pp 3568–3580. (http://dx.doi.org/10.1016/j.jmatprotec.2008.08.015).

5) "Transient liquid phase bonding of 6061-15 wt% SiCp in argon environment using Cu powder interlayer": J. Maity, T.K. Pal, and R. Maiti, Materials Science and Technology, Maney, Vol. 25, No. 12, 2009, pp 1489- 1494. (DOI: 10.1179/174328409X407551).

6) "Isothermal grain growth of austenite in hypoeutectoid and hypereutectoid plain carbon steels": Joydeep Maity and Dipak Kumar Mondal, Journal of Iron and Steel Research International, Elsevier; Vol.17, No.7, 2010, page: 38-43.

7) "Transient liquid phase diffusion bonding of 6061-13 vol.% SiCp composite using Cu powder interlayer: mechanism and interface characterization": J. Maity, T.K. Pal, and R. Maiti, Journal of Materials Science; Vol. 45, Issue No. 13, 2010, pp 3575-3587; DOI 10.1007/s10853-010-4402-y.

8) "Kinetics of transient liquid phase diffusion bonding process for joining aluminium metal matrix composite": S.C. Barman, T.K. Pal and J. Maity – accepted for publication in Materials Science and Technology, Maney, accepted on 16th April, 2010, appeared or available online: June 21, 2010; DOI: 10.1179/026708310X12712410311893.

9) "An alternate approach to accelerated spheroidization in steel by cyclic annealing": Atanu Saha, Dipak Kumar Mondal and Joydeep Maity, accepted for publication in Journal of Materials Engineering and Performance, ASM international; accepted on 27th March, 2010; DOI: 10.1007/s11665-010-9653-x (published online on 27th April, 2010).

10) "Effect of cyclic heat treatment on microstructure and mechanical properties of 0.6 wt% carbon steel": Atanu Saha, Dipak Kumar Mondal and Joydeep Maity, Materials Science and Engineering: A, Elsevier, Vol. 527, Issue No. 16-17 (June), 2010, pp 4001–4007; doi:10.1016/j.msea.2010.03.003.

11) "Morphological changes during annealing of electrodeposited Ni-Cr coating on steel and its effect on corrosion in 3% NaCl solution": M.S. Marwah, V. Srinivas, A.K. Pandey, S.R. Kumar, K. Biswas, and J. Maity- accepted for publication (on May 21, 2010) in the Journal of Iron and Steel Research International, Elsevier.

12) "A Study on Mechanism of Transient Liquid Phase Diffusion Bonding of Aluminium Based Metal Matrix Composite": J. Maity and T.K. Pal- Published in the proceedings of International Welding Symposium (IWS 2k8) on 'Advances in Materials and Joining Challenges and opportunities', February 13-15, 2008, Indian Welding Society, New Delhi, INDIA.

13) "Joining of 6061-15 wt% SiCp by TLP Diffusion Bonding Process using Copper Foil and Copper Powder Interlayer": Joydeep Maity and Tapan Kumar Pal, NMD-ATM 2009, International Symposium on 'Emerging Challenges for Metals and Materials: Engineering and Technology', 14th -17th November (presented on 17th November), Science City, Kolkata, Indian Institute of Metals.

In: Materials Science Researcher Biographical Sketches …   ISBN: 978-1-61942-153-0

Editors: Satomi Matsumoto and Ueda Iwate   © 2013 Nova Science Publishers, Inc.

Chapter 13

BIOGRAPHICAL SKETCH

Irina Meshkova, Ph.D.

Affiliation: Semenov Institute of Chemical Physics of Russian Academy of Sciences, Russia

Date of Birth: 17.09.1933

Education

Institution and Location	Degree	Year Conferred	Scientific Field
Semenov Institute of Chemical Physics of Russian Academy of Sciences, Russia	Ph.D.		Chemistry

Contact Points

Address: 119991 Moscow, Kosygin str.4, Russia

Research and Professional Experience

Kinetic and mechanism of the catalytic olefin polymerization, properties and applications of polyolefin and polyolefin composites

Professional Appointments

Leading scientist

Publication Last 3 years

1) ` "Effect of the Zeolite Support on the Polymerization of propylene with immobilized *ansa*-Zirconocene Catalysts". I.N.Meshkova, O.I.Kudinova, N.Yu.Kovaleva, V.G.

Grinev, E.V.Kiseleva, T.A.Ladygina and L.A.Novokshonova Polymer Science, Ser.B 2009, Vol.51, 9-10, pp. 401-408.

2) ` "Properties of mechanically activated natural clinoptilolite and chabazite " V.A. Nikashina, A.N. Streletsky, I.V. Kolbanev, I.N. Meshkova, V.G.Grinev, I.B.Serova. T.S.Yusupov and L.G.Shumskaya Clay Mineral, 2011, Vol.46, pp.329-337.

3) ` "Applications of synthetic and natural zeolites for creation of supported catalysts of olefin polymerization and composite materials on the base of polyolefin." I.N.Meshkova, V.G.Grinev, T.M.Ushakova, V.A.Nikashina, N.Yu. Kovaleva and L.A.Novokshonova Proceedings of 6th Zeolite Conference, Zvenigorod of Moscow region, June 2011, pp.102-103.

In: Materials Science Researcher Biographical Sketches …   ISBN: 978-1-61942-153-0

Editors: Satomi Matsumoto and Ueda Iwate   © 2013 Nova Science Publishers, Inc.

Chapter 14

BIOGRAPHICAL SKETCH

Manijeh Razeghi, Ph.D.

Date of Birth: April 28, 1943

Education

Institution and Location	Degree	Year Conferred	Scientific Field
Université de Paris, France	Docteur	1980	d'État ès Sciences Physiques
Université de Paris, France	Docteur	1977	3ème Cycle, Solid State Physics
Université de Paris, France	DEA	1976	Science des Matériaux

Contact Points

Northwestern University
Center for Quantum Devices (CQD)
Electrical Engineering and Computer Science (EECS)
Department 2220 Campus Drive, Cook Hall Room 4051
Evanston, IL 60208
Tel: 847-491-7251
FAX: 847-467-1817
Email: razeghi@eecs.northwestern.edu

Research and Professional Experience

1993-present: Adjunct Professor, College of Optical Sciences, University of Arizona 1991-present Walter P. Murphy Professor of Electrical Engineering and Computer Science, and Director, Center for Quantum Devices, Northwestern University, Evanston, IL 2008-

present Global Ambassador for France, McCormick School of Engineering and Applied Science, Northwestern University, Evanston, IL

1986-1991: Head, Exploratory Materials Lab, Thomson-CSF, Orsay, France

1989-1990: Invited Professor, Ecole Polytechnique Federale de Lausanne, France

1986: Invited Professor, University of Michigan-Ann Arbor, MI

1981-1985: Senior Research Scientist, Thomson-CSF, Orsay, France

Professional Appointments

1993-present: Adjunct Professor, College of Optical Sciences, University of Arizona 1991-present Walter P. Murphy Professor of Electrical Engineering and Computer Science, and Director, Center for Quantum Devices, Northwestern University, Evanston, IL 2008-present Global Ambassador for France, McCormick School of Engineering and Applied Science, Northwestern University, Evanston, IL

1986-1992: Head, Exploratory Materials Lab, Thomson-CSF, Orsay, France

1989-1990: Invited Professor, Ecole Polytechnique Federale de Lausanne, France

1986: Invited Professor, University of Michigan-Ann Arbor, MI

1981-1985: Senior Research Scientist, Thomson-CSF, Orsay, France

Honors

- Elected Fellow of Materials Research Society (MRS) – 2008
- Featured in SPIE 2008 Women in Optics Planner Calendar and on cover
- Supervised Best Student Paper Award – Yanbo Bai, "Electrically pumped photonic crystal distributed feedback quantum cascade lasers," SPIE Photonics West Symposium, San Jose, CA, January 2008
- Best Paper Award at the 25th Army Science Conference, Orlando, FL, "Infrared Imaging with Self-Assembled InGaSb Quantum Dot Infrared Detectors" – November 2006
- Supervised research training period award, "Prix de la Fondation from Ecole Polytechnique, France," presented to Pierre-Yves Delaunay for research project entitled, "Infrared Focal Plane Arrays" – November 2005
- Elected Fellow of Institute of Electrical and Electronics Engineers (IEEE) - 2005
- Elected Fellow of Institute of Physics (IOP) - 2005
- Elected Fellow of American Physical Society (APS) - 2004
- Elected Fellow of Optical Society of America (OSA) - 2004
- R.F. Bunshah Award from Int[al] Conference on Metallurgical Coatings and Thin Films - 2004 - Photonics West Optoelectronics '04 Symposium Best Paper Award - 2004
- Nominated for Northwestern University McCormick Teacher of the Year Award – 2003
- Elected Fellow of International Engineering Consortium (IEC) - 2003
- Elected Fellow of Society of Photo-Optical Instrumentation Engineers (SPIE) - 2000 - Photonics West Optoelectronics '98 Symposium Best Paper Award - 1998
- Elected Fellow of Society of Women Engineers - 1995
- Society of Women Engineers (SWE) Achievement Award - 1995
- IBM Europe Science and Technology Prize - 1987

Publications during last three years

1) E.K. Huang, P.Y. Delaunay, B.M. Nguyen, S. Abdollahi Pour, and M. Razeghi, "Photovoltaic MWIR Type-II Superlattice Focal Plane Array on GaAs Substrate," IEEE Journal of Quantum Electronics (JQE), December 2010, Vol. 46, No. 12, p. 1704-1708.

2) C. Bayram, Z. Vashaei, and M. Razeghi, "Reliability in room temperature negative differential resistance characteristics of low-aluminium-content AlGaN/GaN double-barrier resonant tunneling diodes," to appear in Applied Physics Letters.

3) P. Manurkar, S.R. Darvish, B.M. Nguyen, M. Razeghi, and J. Hubbs, "High performance long wavelength Infrared mega-pixel focal plane array based on type-II superlattices," to appear in Applied Physics Letters.

4) J.S. Yu, S. Slivken, and M. Razeghi, "Injector doping level dependent continuous-wave operation of InP-based QCLs at ë~ 7.3 ìm above room temperature," to appear in Semiconductor Science and Technology.

5) M. Razeghi, Y. Bai, S. Slivken and S.R. Darvish, "High performance mid-infrared quantum cascade lasers at Northwestern University," to appear in SPIE Special Issue of Optical Engineering on Quantum and Interband Cascade Lasers, November 2010, Vol. 49, No. 11.

6) B. Gökden, Y. Bai, N. Bandyopadhyay, S. Slivken, and M. Razeghi, "Broad area photonic crystal distributed feedback quantum cascade lasers emitting 34 W at λ ~ 4.36 μm," Applied Physics Letters, 27 September 2010, Vol. 97, No. 13, p. 131112-1.

7) N. Bandyopadhyay, Y. Bai, B. Gokden, A. Myzaferi, S. Tsao, S. Slivken and M. Razeghi, "Watt level performance of quantum cascade lasers in room temperature continuous wave operation at ë ~ 3.76 mm," Applied Physics Letters, 27 September 2010, Vol. 97, No. 13, p. 131117-1.

8) Z. Vashaei, C. Bayram, P. Lavenus, and M. Razeghi, "Photoluminescence characteristics of polar and nonpolar AlGaN/GaN superlattices," Applied Physics Letters, 20 September 2010, Vol. 97, No. 12, p. 121918-1.

9) C. Bayram, Z. Vashaei, and M. Razeghi, "Room temperature negative differential resistance characteristics of polar III-nitride resonant tunneling diodes," Applied Physics Letters, 30 August 2010, Vol. 97, No. 9, p. 092104-1.

10) R. McClintock, E. Cicek, Z. Vashaei, C. Bayram, M. Razeghi and M. Ulmer, "III-nitride based avalanche photo detectors," SPIE Conference, August 1-5, 2010, San Diego, CA Proceedings – Detectors and Imaging Devices: Infrared, Focal plane and Single Photon, Vol. 7780, p. 77801B.

11) E. Cicek, Z. Vashaei, C. Bayram, R. McClintock, M. Razeghi and M. Ulmer, "Comparison of ultraviolet APDs grown on free-standing GaN and sapphire substrates," SPIE Conference, August 1-5, 2010, San Diego, CA Proceedings – Detectors and Imaging Devices: Infrared, Focal plane and Single Photon, Vol. 7780, p. 77801P.

12) E. Cicek, Z. Vashaei, R. McClintock, C. Bayram and M. Razeghi, "Geiger-mode operation of ultraviolet avalanche photodiodes grown on sapphire and free-standing GaN substrates," Applied Physics Letters, 28 June 2010, Vol. 96, No. 26, p. 261107-1.

13) Z. Vashaei, E. Cicek, C. Bayram, R. McClintock and M. Razeghi, "GaN avalanche photodiodes grown on m-plane freestanding GaN substrate," Applied Physics Letters, 17 May 2010, Vol. 96, No. 20, p. 201908-1.

14) M. Razeghi, E.K. Huang, B.M. Nguyen, S. Abdollahi Pour and P.Y. Delaunay, "Type-II antimonide-based superlattices for the third generation infrared focal plane arrays," SPIE Conference, April 5-9, 2010, Orlando, FL Proceedings – Infrared Technology and Applications XXXVI, Vol. 7660, p. 76601F.

15) M. Razeghi, C. Bayram, R. McClintock, F. Hosseini Teherani, D.J. Rogers and V.E. Sandana, "Novel Green Light Emitting Diodes: Exploring Droop-Free Lighting Solutions for a Sustainable Earth," Journal of Light Emitting Diodes, Vol. 2, No. 1, April 2010, p. 1-33.

16) Z. Vashaei, C. Bayram, and M. Razeghi, "Demonstration of negative differential resistance in GaN/AlN resonant tunneling diodes at room temperature," Journal of Applied Physics, 15 April 2010, Vol. 107, no. 8, p. 083505.

17) P.Y. Delaunay and M. Razeghi, "Spatial noise and correctability of Type-II InAs/GaSb focal
plane arrays," IEEE Journal of Quantum Electronics, April 2010, Vol. 46, No. 4, p. 584-588.

18) Y. Bai, S. Slivken, S. Kuboya, S.R. Darvish, and M. Razeghi, "Quantum cascade lasers that emit more light than heat," Nature Photonics, February 2010, Vol. 4, p. 99-102.

19) J.L. Pau, J. Piqueras, D.J. Rogers, F. Hosseini Teherani, K. Minder, R. McClintock, and M. Razeghi, "On the interface properties of ZnO/Si electroluminescent diodes," Journal of Applied Physics, 1 February 2010, Vol. 107, No. 3, p. 033719-1

20) M. Razeghi and B.M. Nguyen, "Band gap tenability of Type II Antimonide-based superlattices," Proceedings of 14th International Conference on Narrow Gap Semiconductors and Systems \ (NGSS-14), Sendai, Japan, July 13-17, 2009, Physics Procedia, Vol. 3, Issue 2, 31 January 2010, p. 1207-1212

21) C. Bayram, Z. Vashaei, and M. Razeghi, "AlN/GaN double-barrier resonant tunneling diodes grown by metal-organic chemical vapor deposition," Applied Physics Letters, 25 January 2010, Vol. 96, No. 4, p. 042103-1.

22) S. Tsao, A. Myzaferi, and M. Razeghi, "High performance quantum dot-quantum well infrared focal plane arrays," SPIE Photonics West, January 22-28, 2010, San Francisco, CA Proceedings – Optoelectronic Integrated Circuits XII, Vol. 7605, p. 76050J-1.

23) D.J. Rogers, F. Hosseini Teherani, V.E. Sandana, and M. Razeghi, "ZnO thin films & nanostructures for emerging optotlectronic applications," SPIE Photonics West, January 22-28, 2010, San Francisco, CA Proceedings – Optoelectronic Integrated Circuits XII, Vol. 7605, p. 76050K-1.

24) B. Gokden, S. Slivken, and M. Razeghi, "High power photonic crystal distributed feedback quantum cascade lasers emitting at 4.5 mm," SPIE Photonics West, January 22-28, 2010, San Francisco, CA Proceedings – Quantum Sensing and Nanophotonic Devices VII, Vol. 7608, p. 760806-1.

25) S. Slivken, Y. Bai, B. Gokden, S.R. Darvish and M. Razeghi, "Current status and potential of high power mid-infrared intersubband lasers," SPIE Photonics West, January 22-28, 2010, San Francisco, CA Proceedings – Quantum Sensing and Nanophotonic Devices VII, Vol. 7608, p. 76080B-1.

26) Y. Bai, S. Slivken, S.R. Darvish and M. Razeghi, "Very high wall plug efficiency of quantum cascade lasers," SPIE Photonics West, January 22-28, 2010, San Francisco, CA Proceedings – Quantum Sensing and Nanophotonic Devices VII, Vol. 7608, p. 76080F-1.

27) M. Razeghi, B.M. Nguyen, P.Y. Delaunay, S. Abdollahi Pour, E.K.W. Huang, P. Manukar, S. Bogdanov, and G. Chen, "High operating temperature MWIR photo detectors based on Type II InAs/GaSb superlattice," SPIE Photonics West, January 22-28, 2010, San Francisco, CA Proceedings – Quantum Sensing and Nanophotonic Devices VII, Vol. 7608, p. 76081Q-1.

28) B.M. Nguyen, S. Abdollahi Pour, S. Bogdanov, and M. Razeghi, "Minority electron unipolar photodetectors based on Type II InAs/GaSb/AlSb superlattices for very long wavelength infrared detection," SPIE Photonics West, January 22-28, 2010, San Francisco, CA Proceedings – Quantum Sensing and Nanophotonic Devices VII, Vol. 7608, p. 760825-1.

29) Razeghi, S. Slivken, Y. Bai, B. Gokden, S.R. Darvish, "High Power Quantum Cascade Lasers," special issue "Advanced Semiconductor Heterostructures for Optoelectronics," New Journal of Physics (NJP), Volume 11, December 2009, p. 125017.

30) Y. Bai, S. Slivken, S.R. Darvish, A. Haddadi, B. Gokden, and M. Razeghi, "High power broad area quantum cascade lasers," Applied Physics Letters, 30 November 2009, Vol. 95, No. 22, p. 221104-1.

31) C. Bayram, N. Pere-Laperne, and M. Razeghi, "Effects of growth temperature and well width on optical and structural characteristics of AlN/GaN superlattices grown by metal-organic chemical vapor deposition," Applied Physics Letters, 16 November 2009, Vol. 95, No. 20, p. 201906.

32) B.M. Nguyen, S. Bogdanov, S. Abdollahi Pour, and M. Razeghi, "Minority electron unipolar photodetectors based on Type II superlattice for very long wavelength infrared detection," Applied Physics Letters, 2 November 2009, Vol. 95, No. 18, p. 183502.

33) S. Abdollahi Pour, B-M. Nguyen, S. Bogdanov, E.K. Huang and M. Razeghi, "Demonstration of high performance long wavelength infrared Type II InAs/GaSb superlattice photodiode grown on GaAs substrate," Applied Physics Letters, 26 October 2009, Vol. 95, No. 17, p. 173505.

34) P.Y. Delaunay and M. Razeghi, "Noise Analysis in Type-II InAs/GaSb Focal Plane Arrays," Virtual Journal of Nanoscale Science & Technology, 5 October 2009, Vol. 20, No. 14.

35) Pere-Laperne, C. Bayram, L. Nguyen-The, R. McClintock and M. Razeghi, "Tunability of intersubband absorption from 4.5 to 5.3 μm in a $_{GaN/Al0.2Ga0.8N}$ superlattices grown by metalorganic chemical vapor deposition, " Applied Physics Letters, 28 September 2009, Vol. 95, No. 13, p. 131109.

36) P.Y. Delaunay and M. Razeghi, "Noise Analysis in Type-II InAs/GaSb Focal Plane Arrays," Journal of Applied Physics, 15 September 2009, Vol. 106, Issue 6, p. 063110.

37) T. Yamanaka, B. Movaghar, S. Tsao, S. Kuboya, A. Myzaferi and M. Razeghi, "Gain-length scaling in quantum dot/quantum well infrared photodetectors," Virtual Journal of Nanoscale Science & Technology, 14 September 2009, Vol. 20, No. 11.

38) C. Bayram and M. Razeghi, "Ultraviolet Detectors: Nitrides push performance of UV Photodidoes," Laser Focus World, September 2009, Vol. 45, Issue 9, p. 47-51.

39)   J.S. Yu, H.K. Lee, S. Slivken, and M. Razeghi, "Thermal characteristics and analysis of quantum cascade lasers for biochemical sensing applications," SPIE Conference, August 2-6, 2009, San Diego, CA Proceedings – Biosensing II, Vol. 7397, p. 739705F-1.

40)   T. Yamanaka, B. Movaghar, S. Tsao, S. Kuboya, A. Myzaferi and M. Razeghi, "Gain-length scaling in quantum dot/quantum well infrared photodetectors," Applied Physics Letters, 31 August 2009, Vol. 95, No. 9, p. 093502-1

41)   M. Razeghi, "Superlattices see in the dark," SPIE Newsroom http://spie.org/x36271 .xml?highlight=x2410&ArticleID=x36271, 28 July 2009.

42)   Y. Bai, B. Gokden, S.R. Darvish, S. Slivken, and M. Razeghi, "Photonic crystal distributed feedback quantum cascade lasers with 12 W output power," Applied Physics Letters, 20 July 2009, Vol. 95, No. 3, p. 031105-1

43)   C. Bayram and M. Razeghi, "Stranski-Krastanov growth of InGaN quantum dots emitting in green spectra," Applied Physics A: Materials Science and Processing, Vol. 96, No. 2, August 2009, p. 403-408.

44)   B.M. Nguyen, D. Hoffman, E.K. Huang, S. Bogdanov, P.Y. Delaunay, M. Razeghi and M. Tidrow, "Demonstration of mid-infrared type II InAs/GaSb superlattice photodiodes grown on GaAs substrate," Applied Physics Letters, 8 June 2009, Vol. 94, No. 22, p. 223506-1

45)   M. Razeghi, D. Hoffman, B.M. Nguyen, P.Y. Delaunay, E.K. Huang, M. Tidrow, and V. Nathan, "Recent Advances in LWIR Type-II InAs/GaSb Superlattice Photodetectors and Focal Plane Arrays at the Center for Quantum Devices, " Proceedings of the IEEE Journal on Optics and Photonics for Defense and Security, Vol. 97, No. 6, June 2009, p. 1056-1066.

46)   M. Razeghi and C. Bayram, "Material and design engineering of (Al)GaN for high-performance avalanche photodiodes and intersubband applications," SPIE Conference, May 4-6, 2009, Dresden, Germany Proceedings – Photonic Materials, Devices and Applications III, Vol. 7366, p. 73661F-1.

47)   M. Razeghi and R. McClintock, "A Review of III-Nitride Research at the Center for Quantum Devices," Proceedings of 2nd International Symposium on Growth of III-Nitrides (ISGN-2), Laforet Shuzenji Izu, Japan, July 6-9, 2008, Journal of Crystal Growth, 1 May 2009, Vol. 311, No. 10, p. 3067-3074

48)   M. Razeghi, "High Performance InP-Based Mid-Infrared Quantum Cascade Lasers," IEEE Journal of Selected Topics in Quantum Electronics: Semiconductor Lasers, Vol. 15, Issue 3, May/June 2009, p. 941-951.

49)   D.J. Rogers, F. Hosseini Teherani, T. Moudakir, S. Gautier, F. Jomard, M. Molinari, M. Troyon, D. McGrouther, J.N. Chapman, M. Razeghi and A. Ougazzaden, "Microstructural compositional, and optical characterization of GaN grown by metal organic vapor phase epitaxy on ZnO epilayers," Journal of Vacuum Science and Technology B, Vol. 27, No. 3, May/June 2009, p. 1655-1657.

50)   C. Bayram, D.J. Rogers, F. Hosseini Teherani, and M. Razeghi, "Fabrication and Characterization of Novel Hybrid Green LEDs based on Substituting n-type ZnO for n-type GaN in an Inverted p-n Junction," Journal of Vacuum Science and Technology B, Vol. 27, No. 3, May/June 2009, p. 1784-1788.

51)   V. E. Sandana, D. J. Rogers, F. H. Teherani, R. McClintock, C.Bayram, M. Razeghi, H.-J. Drouhin, M.C. Clochard, V. Sallet, G. Garry, and F. Falyouni, "Comparison of

ZnO Nanostructures Grown Using pulsed layer deposition, metalorganic chemical vapor deposition, and physical vapor transport", Journal of Vacuum Science and Technology B, Vol. 27, No. 3, May/June 2009, p. 1678-1683.

52) B.M. Nguyen, D. Hoffman, E.K. Huang, P.Y. Delaunay, and M. Razeghi, "High performance antimony based type-II superlattice photodiodes on GaAs substrate," SPIE Conference, April 13- 17, 2009, Orlando, FL Proceedings – Infrared Technology and Applications XXXV, Vol. 7298, p. 72981T.

53) P.Y. Delaunay, B.M. Nguyen and M. Razeghi, "Background limited performance of long wavelength infrared focal plane arrays fabricated from type-II InAs/GaSb M-structure superlattice," SPIE Conference, April 13-17, 2009, Orlando, FL Proceedings – Infrared Technology and Applications XXXV, Vol. 7298, p. 72981Q.

54) C. Bayram, N. Pere-Laperne, R. McClintock, B. Fain and M. Razeghi, "Pulsed metalorganic chemical vapor deposition of high quality AlN/GaN superlattices for near-infrared intersubband transitions, " Applied Physics Letters, 23 March 2009, Vol. 94, No. 12, p. 121902-1.

55) P.Y. Delaunay, B.M. Nguyen, D. Hoffman, E.K. Huang and M. Razeghi, "Background limited performance of long wavelength infrared focal plane arrays fabricated from M-structure InAs- GaSb superlattices," IEEE Journal of Quantum Electronics, Vol. 45, No. 2, February 2009, p. 157-162

56) E.K. Huang, D. Hoffman, B.M. Nguyen, P.Y. Delaunay and M. Razeghi, "Surface leakage reduction in narrow band gap type-II antimonide-base superlattice photodiodes," Applied Physics Letters, 94 (5), 2 February 2009, p. 053506-1.

57) H.K. Lee, K.S. Chung, J.S. Yu and M. Razeghi, "Thermal analysis of buried heterostructure quantum cascade lasers for long wavelength infrared emission using 2D anisotropic heat dissipation model," Physica Status Solidi (a), Vol. 206, February 2009, p. 356-362

58) R. McClintock, J.L. Pau, C. Bayram, B. Fain, P. Giedratis, M. Razeghi and M. Ulmer, "III- Nitride avalance photodiodes," SPIE Conference, January 25-29, 2009, San Jose, CA Proceedings – Quantum Sensing and Nanophotonic Devices VI, Vol. 7222, p. 7222-0U.

59) Y. Bai, B. Gokden, S. Slivken, S.R. Darvish, S.A. Pour and M. Razeghi, "Mid-infrared quantum cascade lasers with high wall plug efficiency," SPIE Conference, January 25-29, 2009, San Jose, CA Proceedings – Quantum Sensing and Nanophotonic Devices VI, Vol. 7222, p. 7222-0O.

60) C. Bayram, B. Fain, N. Pere-Laperne, R. McClintock and M. Razeghi, "Pulsed metalorganic chemical vapor deposition of high quality AlN/GaN superlattices for intersubband transitions," SPIE Conference, January 25-29, 2009, San Jose, CA Proceedings – Quantum Sensing and Nanophotonic Devices VI, Vol. 7222, p. 7222-12.

61) J.L. Pau, C. Bayram, P. Giedraitis, R. McClintock, and M. Razeghi, "GaN-based nanostructured photodetectors," SPIE Conference, January 25-29, 2009, San Jose, CA Proceedings – Quantum Sensing and Nanophotonic Devices VI, Vol. 7222, p. 7222-14.

62) Hoffman, B.M. Nguyen, E.K. Huang, P.Y. Delaunay, S. Bogdanov, P. Manurkar, M. Razeghi, and V. Nathan, "The importance of band alignment in VLWIR type-II InAs/GaSb heterodiodes containing the M-structure barrier," SPIE Conference, January 25-29, 2009, San Jose, CA Proceedings – Quantum Sensing and Nanophotonic Devices VI, Vol. 7222, p. 7222-15.

63)   P.Y. Delaunay, B.M. Nguyen, D. Hoffman, E.K. Huang, P. Manurkar, S. Bogdanov
       and M. Razeghi, "Background limited performance of long wavelength infrared focal
       plane arrays fabricated from M-structure InAs/GaSb superlattices," SPIE Conference,
       January 25-29, 2009, San Jose, CA Proceedings – Quantum Sensing and Nanophotonic
       Devices VI, Vol. 7222, p. 7222-0W.

64)   E.K. Huang, B.M. Nguyen, D. Hoffman, P.Y. Delaunay and M. Razeghi, "Inductively
       coupled plasma etching and processing techniques for type-II InAs/GaSb superlattices
       infrared detectors toward high fill factor focal plane arrays," SPIE Conference, January
       25-29, 2009, San Jose, CA Proceedings – Quantum Sensing and Nanophotonic Devices
       VI, Vol. 7222, p. 7222-0Z.

65)   C. Bayram, F.H. Teherani, D.J. Rogers and M. Razeghi, "Hybrid green LEDs based on
       n- ZnO/(InGaN/GaN) multi-quantum-wells/p-GaN," SPIE Conference, January 25-29,
       2009, San Jose, CA Proceedings – Zinc Oxide Materials and Devices IV, Vol. 7217, p.
       7217-0P.

66)   S. Tsao, T. Yamanaka, S.A. Pour, I-K. Park, B. Movaghar and M. Razeghi, "Quantum
       dot in a well infrared photodetectors for high operating temperature focal plane arrays,"
       SPIE Conference, January 25-29, 2009, San Jose, CA Proceedings – Quantum Dots,
       Particles and Nanoclusters VI, Vol. 7224, p. 7224-0V.

67)   M. Razeghi, "High-power high-wall plug efficiency mid-infrared quantum cascade
       lasers based on InP/GaInAs/InAlAs material system," SPIE Conference, January 25-
       29, 2009, San Jose, CA Proceedings – Novel In-Plane Semiconductor Lasers VIII, Vol.
       7230, p. 7230-11.

68)   J.L. Pau, C. Bayram, R. McClintock and M. Razeghi, "GaN nanostructred p-i-n
       photodiodes," Applied Physics Letters, 93 (22), 1 December 2008, p. 221104-1.

69)   C. Bayram, J.L. Pau, R. McClintock, and M. Razeghi, "Comprehensive study of blue
       and green multi-quantum-well light emitting diodes grown on conventional and lateral
       epitaxial overgrowth GaN," Applied Physics B-Lasers and Optics, Vol. 95, 29
       November 2008, p. 307-314.

70)   C. Bayram, J.L. Pau, R. McClintock, M. Razeghi, M.P. Ulmer, and D. Silversmith,
       "High quantum efficiency back-illuminated GaN avalanche photodiodes," Applied
       Physics Letters, 93 (21), 24 November 2008, p. 211107-1.

71)   J.S. Yu, S. Slivken, A. Evans, and M. Razeghi, "High-Performance, Continuous-Wave
       Quantum-Cascade Lasers Operating up to 85^0C at $1 \sim 8.8$ mm," Applied Physics A:
       Materials Science & Processing, Vol 93, No. 2, November 2008, p. 405-408.

72)   B.M. Nguyen, D. Hoffman, P.Y. Delaunay, E.K. Huang, M. Razeghi and J. Pellegrino,
       "Band edge tunability of M-structure for heterojunction design in Sb based Type II
       superlattice photodiodes," Applied Physics Letters, 93 (16), 20 October 2008, p.
       163502-1.

73)   C. Bayram, J.L. Pau, R. McClintock, and M. Razeghi, "Delta-doping optimization for
       high quality p-type GaN," Journal of Applied Physics, 104 (8), 15 October 2008, p.
       083512-1.

74)   S. Slivken, Y. Bai, S.R. Darvish and M. Razeghi, "Powerful QCLs eye remote
       sensing," Compound Semiconductor Magazine, Vol. 14 No. 9, October 2008, p. 21-23

75)   B. Movaghar, S. Tsao, S. Abdollahi Pour, T. Yamanaka, and M. Razeghi, "Gain and
       recombination dynamics in photodetectors made with quantum nanostructures: the

quantum dot in a well and the quantum well," Virtual Journal of Nanoscale Science & Technology, Vol. 18, No. 14, 6 October 2008.

76) M. Razeghi, "Quantum Devices based on Modern Band Structure Engineering and Epitaxial Technology," Modern Physics Letters B, Vol. 22 No. 24, 20 September 2008, p. 2343-2371.

77) B.M. Nguyen, D. Hoffman, E.K. Huang, P.Y. Delaunay, and M. Razeghi, "Background limited long wavelength infrared Type-II InAs/GaSb superlattice photodiodes operating at 110K," Applied Physics Letters, 93 (12), 22 September 2008, p. 123502-1.

78) B. Movaghar, S. Tsao, S. Abdollahi Pour, T. Yamanaka, and M. Razeghi, "Gain and recombination dynamics in photodetectors made with quantum nanostructures: the quantum dot in a well and the quantum well," Physical Review B, Vol. 78, No. 11, 15 September 2008, p. 115320-1

79) Bayram, F.H. Teherani, D.J. Rogers and M. Razeghi, "A hybrid green light-emitting diode comprised of n-ZnO/(InGaN/GaN) multi-quantum wells/p-GaN," Applied Physics Letters, 93 (8), 25 August 2008, p. 081111-1.

80) J.S. Yu, S. Slivken, A. Evans, and M. Razeghi, "High-Performance Continuous-Wave Operation of $l \sim 4.6$ mm Quantum-Cascade Lasers Above Room Temperature," IEEE Journal of Quantum Electronics, Vol. 44, No. 8, August 2008, p. 747-754

81) M. Razeghi, B.M. Nguyen, D. Hoffman, P.Y. Delaunay, E.K. Huang, M.Z. Tidrow, and V. Nathan, "Development of material quality and structural design for high performance type-II InAs/GaSb superlattice photodiodes and focal plane arrays," SPIE Conference, August 11-14, 2008, San Diego, CA Proceedings – Infrared Spaceborne remote Sensing and Instrumentation XVI, Vol. 7082, p. 708204.

82) B.M. Nguyen, D. Hoffman, P.Y. Delaunay, E.K. Huang, and M. Razeghi, "Very high performance LWIR and VLWIR type-II InAs/GaSb superlattice photodiodes with M-structure barrier," SPIE Conference, August 11-14, 2008, San Diego, CA Proceedings – Infrared Spaceborne remote Sensing and Instrumentation XVI, Vol. 7082, p. 708205.

83) Hoffman, B.M. Nguyen, E.K. Huang, P.Y. Delaunay, M. Razeghi, M. Tidrow, and J. Pellegrino, "The Effect of Doping the M-Barrier in VLWIR Type-II InAs/GaSb Heterodiodes," Applied Physics Letters, 93 (3), 21 July 2008, p. 031107-1

84) Y. Bai, S. Slivken, S.R. Darvish and M. Razeghi, "Room temperature continuous wave operation of quantum cascade lasers with 12.5% wall plug efficiency," Applied Physics Letters, 93 (2), 14 July 2008, p. 021103-1.

85) M. Razeghi, "Type II superlattices could be the next solution for fast and uniform infrared imaging," SPIE Professional Magazine, July 2008.

86) D.J. Rogers, D.C. Look, F.H. Teherani, K. Minder, M. Razeghi, A. Largeteau, G. Demazeau, J. Morrod, K.A. Prior, A. Lusson, and S. Hassani, "Investigations of ZnO thin films grown on c- Al2O3 by pulsed laser deposition in N2 + O2 ambient," Physica Status Solidi (c), Vol. 5, No. 9, July 2008, p. 3084-3087.

87) M. Razeghi, S. Slivken, Y. Bai, and S.R. Darvish, "The Quantum Cascade Laser: A Versatile and Powerful Tool," Optics and Photonics News (OPN) Magazine, July/August 2008, Vol 19, No. 7/8, p. 42-47.

88) C. Bayram, J.L. Pau, R. McClintock, and M. Razeghi, "Performance enhancement of GaN ultraviolet avalanche photodiodes with p-type d–doping," Applied Physics Letters, 92 (24), 16 June 2008, p. 241103-1.

89) S. Tsao, H. Lim, H. Seo, W. Zhang and M. Razeghi, "InP-based quantum-dot infrared photodetectors with high quantum efficiency and high temperature imaging," IEEE Sensors Journal, Special Issue on Nanosensors for Defense and Security, Vol. 8, No. 6, June 2008, p. 936-941.

90) P.Y. Delaunay, B.M. Nguyen, D. Hoffman, A. Hood, E.K. Huang, M. Razeghi and M.Z. Tidrow, "High quantum efficiency two color type-II InAs/GaSb n-i-p-p-i-n photodiodes, " Applied Physics Letters, 92 (11), 17 March 2008, p. 111112-1.

91) M. Razeghi, D. Hoffman, B.M. Nguyen, P.Y. Delaunay, E.K. Huang, and M.Z. Tidrow, "Recent advances in LWIR type-II InAs/GaSb superlattice photodetectors and focal plane arrays at the Center for Quantum Devices," SPIE Conference, March 17-19, 2008, Orlando, FL Proceedings – Infrared Technology and Applications XXXIV, Vol. 6940, p. 694009.

92) P.Y. Delaunay, B.M. Nguyen, D. Hoffman and M. Razeghi, "High performance focal plane array based on InAs/GaSb superlattices with a 10 mm cutoff wavelength," IEEE Journal of Quantum Electronics, Vol. 44, No. 5, May 2008, p. 462-467.

93) J.L. Pau, R. McClintock, C. Bayram, K. Minder, D. Silversmith and M. Razeghi, "High Optical Response in Forward Biased (In, Ga)N-GaN Multiquantum Well Diodes under Barrier Illumination," IEEE Journal of Quantum Electronics, Vol. 44, No. 4, April 2008, p. 346-353.

94) J.L. Pau, C. Bayram, R. McClintock, M. Razeghi, and D. Silversmith "Back-illuminated separate absorption and multiplication GaN avalanche photodiodes," Applied Physics Letters, 92 (10), 10 March 2008, p. 101120-1

95) Y. Bai, S. Slivken, S.R. Darvish, W. Zhang, A. Evans, J. Nguyen and M. Razeghi, "Room temperature continuous wave operation of quantum cascade lasers with watt-level optical power," Applied Physics Letters, 92 (10), 10 March 2008, p. 101105-1

96) McClintock, J.L. Pau, K. Minder, C. Bayram and M. Razeghi, "III-Nitride photon counting avalanche photodiodes," SPIE Conference, January 20-25, 2008, San Jose, CA Proceedings – Quantum Sensing and Nanophotonic Devices V, Vol. 6900, p. 69000N-1-11.

97) P.Y. Delaunay and M. Razeghi, "High performance focal plane array based on type-II InAs/GaSb superlattice heterostructures," SPIE Conference, January 20-25, 2008, San Jose, CA Proceedings – Quantum Sensing and Nanophotonic Devices V, Vol. 6900, p. 69000M-1-10.

98) Slivken, A. Evans, J. Nguyen, Y. Bai, P. Sung, S.R. Darvish, W. Zhang and M. Razeghi, "Overview of Quantum Cascade Laser Research at the Center for Quantum Devices," SPIE Conference, January 20-25, 2008, San Jose, CA Proceedings – Quantum Sensing and Nanophotonic Devices V, Vol. 6900, p. 69000B-1-8.

99) Y. Bai, P. Sung, S.R. Darvish, W. Zhang, A. Evans, S. Slivken, and M. Razeghi, "Electrically pumped photonic crystal distributed feedback quantum cascade lasers," SPIE Conference, January 20-25, 2008, San Jose, CA Proceedings – Quantum Sensing and Nanophotonic Devices V, Vol. 6900, p. 69000A-1-8.

100) A.Hood, A. Evans and M. Razeghi, "Type-II Superlattices and Quantum Cascade Lasers for MWIR and LWIR Free-Space Communications," SPIE Conference, January 20-25, 2008, San Jose, CA Proceedings – Quantum Sensing and Nanophotonic Devices V, Vol. 6900, p. 690005- 1-9.

101) V.E. Sandana, D.J. Rogers, F.H. Teherani, R. McClintock, M. Razeghi, H.J. Drouhin, M.C. Clochard, V. Sallett, G. Garry and F. Fayoud, "MOCVD Growth of ZnO Nanostructures Using Au Droplets as Catalysts," SPIE Conference, January 20-25, 2008, San Jose, CA Proceedings – Zinc Oxide Materials and Devices III, Vol. 6895, p. 68950Z-1-6.

In: Materials Science Researcher Biographical Sketches …   ISBN: 978-1-61942-153-0
Editors: Satomi Matsumoto and Ueda Iwate   © 2013 Nova Science Publishers, Inc.

Chapter 15

BIOGRAPHICAL SKETCH

Mahendra Kumar Samal, Dr.

Date of Birth: 3rd May 1974

Education

Institution and Location	Degree	Year Conferred	Scientific Field
	B.Tech		Mechanical Engineering
	M. Tech.		Mechanical Engineering
	Ph.D		Mechanical Engineering

Contact Points: +91-22-25505151,

E-mail: mksamal@yahoo.com; mksamal@barc.gov.in; samal.3@osu.edu

Research and Professional Experience

14 years of research experience in the following research areas: Continuum damage mechanics, Fracture mechanics, Finite element method, Material constitutive modeling, Modeling of nonlinear behaviour of piezoelectric materials, Development of tools for online monitoring of critical plant components.

Research interests:

Professional Appointments

Senior Scientist, Bhabha Atomic Research Centre, Trombay, Mumbai, India, September 1996 till date.

Visiting Scientist at MaterialprÃ¼fungsanstalt (MPA) and Institut fÃ¼r MaterialprÃ¼fung, Werkstoffkunde und Festigkeitslehre (IMWF), University of Stuttgart, Germany. Aug-Dec 2000, Jan-March 2006, Sep-Dec 2006, Oct-Nov 2007.

Visiting Scientist, Department of Mechanical Engineering, Ohio State University, USA, November 2009 till date

Member, Editorial Board (Journal of Chemical Engineering and Materials Science, International Journal of Physical Sciences of Academic Journals)

Honors

Received Homi Bhabha award and gold medal for securing first rank among mechanical engineering students of Bhabha Atomic research Centre Training School, Year: 1997.

Received Ashok Chaturvedi Memorial prize for becoming the most outstanding student (first rank) among the M.Tech students of mechanical engineering department of Indian Institute of Technology Bombay, Year: 2003.

Received P.M. Natu Memorial prize for becoming the most outstanding student (first rank) among the design engineering M.Tech students of mechanical engineering department of Indian Institute of Technology Bombay, Year: 2003.

Received fellowship offered by German Academic Exchange Service (DAAD) to carry out research at Technical University of Darmstadt, Germany, May 2002-February 2003.

Received the best paper award (along with B.K. Dutta and H.S. Kushwaha) for the paper "Modeling of ductile fracture by Gurson model"• in National Conference on Computational Material Science (NCCMS-2000), Mumbai, India (July 27-28, 2000).

In: Materials Science Researcher Biographical Sketches …   ISBN: 978-1-61942-153-0
Editors: Satomi Matsumoto and Ueda Iwate   © 2013 Nova Science Publishers, Inc.

Chapter 16

BIOGRAPHICAL SKETCH

Felipe Silva Semaan

Affiliation: Department of Analytical Chemistry, Fluminense Federal University, NiterÃ³i, Rio de Janeiro, Brazil

Date of Birth: August 16th 1980

Education

Institution and Location	Degree	Year Conferred	Scientific Field
Alfenas Federal University	Bachelor	1999-2002	Pharmaceutical Sciences
University of SÃ£o Paulo	Doctorate	2004-2007	Sciences - Analytical Chemistry
University of Coimbra	Post-doctorate	2007-2008	Analytical Chemistry

Contact Points

   Address: Fluminense Federal University, Institute of Chemistry, Department of Analytical Chemistry, Outeiro SÃ£o JoÃ£o Batista, s/n, room 2/207, NiterÃ³i, Rio de Janeiro, Brazil, 24020-150.

Research and Professional Experience

Professor of Biophysics at Alfenas Federal University (2003), Professor of Analytical Chemistry at Juiz de Fora Federal University (2009), Professor of Physical-Chemistry at Presidente AntÃ´nio Carlos University (2009), currently Professor of Analytical Chemistry at Fluminense Federal University (since 2009). Experience in Optical and Electroanalytical Flow Analysis, Bioanalysis, Thermal Analysis and Electroanalytical Chemistry.

Professional Appointments

Referee activities for the Journal of Automated Methods and Management in Chemistry, member of Security and Scientific Commissions of Fluminense Federal University, *Ad Hoc* consultant for FACEPE and UNOPAR.

Honors

Member of the International Society of Electrochemistry.

Publications during last three years

Fonseca, C. A., Vaz, G. C. S., Azevedo, J. P. A. Exploiting ion-pair formation for the enhacement of electroanalytical determination of pyridoxine (B6) onto graphite-polyurethane electrodes. Microchemical Journal, *in press*, 2011.

Santos, T. A. D., Costa, D. O., Pita, S. S. R., Semaan, F. S. Potentiometric and conductimetric studies of chemical equilibria for pyridoxine hydrochloride in aqueous solutions: simple experimental determination of pKa values and analytical applications to pharmaceutical analysis. EclÃ©tica QuÃmica, *in press*, 2011.

Sousa, R. A., Semaan, F. S., Cervini, P., Cavalheiro, E. T. G. Determination of minoxidil by the bleaching of a permanganate carrier solution in a flow-based spectrophotometric system. Analytical Letters, v.44, p.349 - 359, 2011.

Semaan, F. S., Cavalheiro, E. T. G., Brett, C. M. A. Electrochemical Behavior of Verapamil at Graphite-Polyurethane Composite Electrodes: Determination of Release Profiles in Pharmaceutical Samples. Analytical Letters, v.42, p.1119 - 1135, 2009.

Nunes, R. S., Semaan, F. S., Riga, A. T., Cavalheiro, E. T. G. Thermal behavior of verapamil hydrochloride and its association with excipients. Journal of Thermal Analysis and Calorimetry, v.97, p.349 - 353, 2009.

Semaan, F. S., Pinto, E. M., Cavalheiro, E. T. G., Brett, C. M. A. A Graphite-Polyurethane Composite Electrode for the Analysis of Furosemide. Electroanalysis, v.20, p.2287 - 2293, 2008.

Semaan, F. S., Nogueira, P. A., Cavalheiro, E. T. G. Flow-based fluorimetric determination of furosemide in pharmaceutical formulations and biological samples: Use of micelar media to improve sensitivity. Analytical Letters, v.41, p.66 - 79, 2008.

In: Materials Science Researcher Biographical Sketches ...   ISBN: 978-1-61942-153-0
Editors: Satomi Matsumoto and Ueda Iwate   © 2013 Nova Science Publishers, Inc.

Chapter 17

BIOGRAPHICAL SKETCH

Irina Shtangeeva, Dr. PhD.

Date of Birth: 01.01.1953

Contact Points: shtangeeva@gmail.com

Research and Professional Experience

My main scientific interests relate to ecology, biogeochemistry, multivariate statistics and modelling, modern analytical techniques. During many years I perform experimental studies on biogeochemistry of trace and ultratrace elements of unknown biological significance. In 2008 we started experiments on the biogeochemistry of antimony.

I am specialist in neutron activation analysis. This unique analytical technique I usually use for elemental analysis of our experimental samples. One of the most interesting for me directions of my work is multivariate statistical treatment of experimental data.

Professional Appointments

2006: senior researcher, Chemical Department, St. Petersburg University
1999 – 2006: senior researcher, Interdisciplinary Center, St. Petersburg University
1991 -1999: senior researcher, laboratory of nuclear analytical techniques, Institute of Earth Crust, St. Petersburg University
1983 -1991: researcher, Institute of Earth Crust, St. Petersburg University
1979 -1983: junior research scientist, Institute of Earth Crust, St. Petersburg University
1978 -1979: engineer, Institute of Earth Crust, St. Petersburg University

Honors

Fellowships (to conduct independent research)

1996: Nordic Council of Ministers Research Scholar, at VTT Chemical Technology (Otaniemi, Finland)

1997: Nordic Council of Ministers Research Scholar, at Risoe National Laboratory (Roskilde, Denmark)

2001: CNRS Research Scholar, at LPS, CEA-CNRS (Saclay, France)

2003: CEA Research Scholar, at LPS, CEA-CNRS (Saclay, France)

2008: DFG Research Scholar, at Hahn Meitner Institut (Berlin, Germany)

2008: Ellen Gledisch Stipend, Norwegian University of Science and Technology (Trondheim, Norway)

2009: International Visiting Fellowship, Sydney University (Australia)

2010: *Triple I* mobility scheme, K.U. Leuven, Belgium

Winner in the platform session of ICOBTE, Uppsala, Sweden, 2003

My biography appeared in the following books

Marquis Who's Who Publications, 2005, 2006 and 2009.

Membership

Member of International Advisory Board of Research Journal of Chemistry and Environment and International Society for Trace Element Biochemistry

Reviewer for International Journals:

- Aquatic Botany
- Chemosphere
- Environ. Toxicol. Chem.
- J. of Radioanal. Nucl. Chem.
- J. of Environ. Exp. Botany
- J. of Environ. Radioact.
- Talanta

Publications Last 3 Years

Book chapters:

I. Shtangeeva. Uranium and thorium accumulation in cultivated plants. In: Trace Elements: Nutritional Benefits, Environmental Contamination and Health, John Wiley & Sons, Inc., USA, 2008, ed. M. N. V. Prasad, p.297-344.

Articles

1) I. Shtangeeva, E. Steinnes, S. Lierhagen. Macronutrients and trace elements in rye and wheat: Similarities and differences in uptake and relationships between elements. Environ. Exp. Botany, in press. doi:10.1016/j.envexpbot.2010.09.013.
2) I. Shtangeeva, A. Harris, R. Bali. Bioavailability and toxicity of antimony. J. of Geochem. Explor., in press. 2010, doi:10.1016/j. gexplo.2010.07.003.
3) I. Shtangeeva. Uranium and thorium in plants. J. Environ. Radioact., 2010, 101, 458-463.
4) I. Shtangeeva, D. Alber, G. Bukalis, B. Stanik, F. Zepezauer. Multivariate statistical analysis applied to distribution of nutrients and trace elements in plants and soil collected in the Northwest region of Russia. Plant and Soil, 2009, 322(1-2), 219-228.
5) I. Shtangeeva, A. TÅ±rler, X. Lin. Thorium and uranium bioaccumulation in wheat and rye plants. Proceedings of 5th International conference on Naturally Occurring Radioactive Material, 2008, p.19-36.
6) I. Shtangeeva. How can we improve phytoremediation efficiency. In: Environmental Geotechnology and Global Sustainable Development, University of Hong-Kong, Hong-Kong, 2008, ed. A. T. Yeung, p.117-126.
7) I. Shtangeeva, J. Laiho, H. Kahelin, V. Surin. Effect of soil fertilisation on uptake of macro- and trace elements by wheat grown in two different soils. J. Plant Nutrition, 2008, v.31, N2, p.395-407.
8) I. Shtangeeva, S. Ayrault. Effects of Eu and Ca on yield and mineral nutrition of wheat *(Triticum aestivum)* seedlings. Environ. Exp. Botany, 2007, v.59, p.49-58.

In: Materials Science Researcher Biographical Sketches ...   ISBN: 978-1-61942-153-0
Editors: Satomi Matsumoto and Ueda Iwate   © 2013 Nova Science Publishers, Inc.

Chapter 18

BIOGRAPHICAL SKETCH

Gabriel Trejo, PhD

Date of Birth: 22-06-1965

Education

Institution and Location	Degree	Year Conferred	Scientific Field
Universidad Nacional Autónoma de México			

Contact Points: gtrejo@cideteq.mx

Research and Professional Experience

My field of specialization is the adsorption of organic molecules onto solids electrodes and the electrodeposition of metals (Zn, Mn, Co, Cu, Ni) and alloys (Zn-Co and Zn-Mn).

Professional Appointments

Researcher

Professional Experience

15 years

Publications during last three years

1) J.C. Ballesteros, P. Díaz-Arista, Y. Meas, R. Ortega, G. Trejo, Zinc Electrodeposition in the Presence of Polyethylene Glycol 20000, Electrochimica Acta 52 (2007) 3686-3696

2) J.L. Ortiz-Aparicio, Y. Meas, G. Trejo, R. Ortega, T.W. Chapman, E. Chainet, P. Ozil, Electrodeposition of zinc-cobalt alloy from a complexing alkaline glycinate bath, Electrochimica Acta 52 (2007) 4742-4751

3) Erika R. Larios Duran, Gabriel Trejo, Thomas W. Chapman and Rene Antaño-López, Estimation of Intrinsic Rate Constants of Electrochemical Adsorption-Desorption Processes from AC Impedance Data, Electrochemical and Solid -State Letters 10 (7) (2007) F27-F29

4) J.L. Ortiz-Aparicio, Y. Meas, G. Trejo, R. Ortega, T.W. Chapman, E. Chainet, P. Ozil, Effect of Quaternary Ammonium Compounds on the electrodeposition of ZnCo alloys from Gluconate Baths, Journal of the Electrochemical Society 155 (3) (2008) D167-D175

5) Méndez, P. Díaz-Arista, L. Salgado, Y. Meas, G. Trejo, EQCM Study of the Adsorption/Desorption Processes of Polyethyleneglycol with Molecular Weight 20,000 on Pt in Perchloric Acid Solution, *Int. J. Electrochem. Sci.*, 3 (2008) 918 - 934

6) P. Díaz-Arista, Z.I. Ortiz, H. Ruiz, R. Ortega, Y. Meas, G. Trejo, Electrodeposition and characterization of Zn–Mn alloy coatings obtained from a chloride-based acidic bath containing ammonium thiocyanate as an additive, Surface and coating Technology, 203 (2009) 1167-1175

7) J.L. Ortíz-Aparicio, Y. Meas, G. Trejo, R. Ortega, T.W. Chapman, E. Chainet, P. Ozil, ZnCo-Electrodeposition baths based on alkaline chloride-gluconate electrolytes containing quaternary ammonium compounds, J. Electrochem. Soc. 156 (2009) K205-K213

8) Z.I. Ortiz, P. Díaz-Arista, Y. Meas, R. Ortega-Borges, G. Trejo, Characterization of the corrosión products of electrodeposited Zn, Zn-Co and Zn-Mn alloys coatings, Corrosion Science 51 (2009) 2703-2715

9) A. Sulcius, E. Griskonis, P. Dias-Arista, G. Trejo, Influence of ammonium selenate and thiourea mixture on mechanical properties and morphology of Zn-Mn alloy coatings electrodeposited from sulphate-citrate bath, Transactions of the Institute of Metal Finishing 87 (5) (2009) 254-258.

10) *J.C. Ballesteros, E. Chaînet, P. Ozil, G. Trejo, Y. Meas,* Initial stages of the electrocrystallization of copper from non-cyanide alkaline bath containing glycine, Journal of Electroanalytical Chemistry, 645 (2010) 94-102

11) *Alia Mendez, L.E. Morón. G. Orozco, Y. Meas, R. Ortega-Borges, G. Trejo,* EQCM Study of the Adsorption of Polyethyleneglycol With Different Molecular Weights and its Coadsorption With Cl- ions on Pt in Perchloric Acid Solution, *Int. J. Electrochem. Sci.,* 5 (2010) 1754 - 1772

In: Materials Science Researcher Biographical Sketches …   ISBN: 978-1-61942-153-0
Editors: Satomi Matsumoto and Ueda Iwate   © 2013 Nova Science Publishers, Inc.

Chapter 19

BIOGRAPHICAL SKETCH

Gerd Weckwerth, Dr.

Date of Birth: 18.4.1954

Education

Institution and Location	Degree	Year Conferred	Scientific Field
Diplom Physiker (physicist) with a PhD in nuclear- and cosmochemistry			

Professional Appointments

Since 1995 Scientific co-worker and lecturer at the institute for Geology and Mineralogy of the University of Cologne

Honors

Substitute of the chair of Inorganic Geochemistry at the RWTH in Aachen

Publications during last three years

Weckwerth, G: Origin of fine dust in urban environmental zones - Evidence from element patterns received by dichotomous collection and INAA Appl. Radiation and Isotopes, V.:68,10, 1878-1883 (2010)

Sokol, A. K., Fernandes, V. A., Schulz, T., Bischoff, A., Burgess, R., Clayton, R. N., Muenker, C., Nishiizumi, K., Palme, H., Schultz, L., Weckwerth, G., Mezger, K., Horstmann, M.: Geochemistry, petrology and ages of the lunar meteorites Kalahari 008 and 009: New constraints on early lunar evolution, GEOCHIMICA ET COSMOCHIMICA ACTA, Vol 72, Issue 19, 4845-4873 (2008)

http://www.bast.de/nn_789794/DE/Publikationen/Veranstaltungen/V3-Luftqualitaet-
2008/luftqualit_C3_A4t.html (Poster at a conference at BAST, Berg.Gladbach 2008)
Further publications in last 3 years are outside the area of geosciences. In close connection: 5
years ago:A German review about ?Antimony in brake-linings?(Von?Asbest zu
Antimon-?), 9 years ago (Nov. 2001) one of the most cited papers in "Atmospheric
Environment" with the title: ?Verification of traffic emitted aerosol components in the
ambient air of Cologne (Germany)?

In: Materials Science Researcher Biographical Sketches …   ISBN: 978-1-61942-153-0
Editors: Satomi Matsumoto and Ueda Iwate   © 2013 Nova Science Publishers, Inc.

Chapter 20

BIOGRAPHICAL SKETCH

Erdong Wu, Ph. D.

Affiliation: Institute of Metal Research, Chinese Academy of Sciences

Date of Birth: 1/13/1951

Education

Institution and Location	Degree	Year Conferred	Scientific Field
	PH. D.		

Address: Wenhua Road 72, Shenyang 110016, China

Research and Professional Experience

Research on material science for more than 20 years

Professional Appointments

Professor at IMR

Publications during last three years

About 10 reviewed papers

In: Materials Science Researcher Biographical Sketches …   ISBN: 978-1-61942-153-0
Editors: Satomi Matsumoto and Ueda Iwate   © 2013 Nova Science Publishers, Inc.

Chapter 21

BIOGRAPHICAL SKETCH

Andriy Yakymovych, Doctor of Philosophy

Date of Birth: 03.03.1981

Education

Institution and Location	Degree	Year Conferred	Scientific Field
Faculty of Physics, Ivan Franko National University, Lviv, Ukraine. Degree work: "Viscosity of liquid Al-Ni-Y alloys"	Master of Sciences in Physics	2003	
Department of Physics of Metals, Ivan Franko National University, Lviv, Ukraine.	Ph.D.	2009	
Thesis: "Fluctuations of concentration in binary metallic liquid alloys with the limited solubility of components". Scientific Adviser – prof. Stepan Mudry (Ivan Franko National University, Lviv, Ukraine)	Ph.D.		

General: physics and chemistry of metallic liquid alloys.
Specific: - high-temperature investigation of metals;
- lead-free solder materials;
- critical phenomena and phase transitions in liquids;
- liquid alloys with a miscibility gap.

Research and Professional Experience

- Investigation of viscosity by oscillating-cup viscosimeter.
- Investigation of enthalpy of mixing with experimental arrangement based on the calorimetric method.

Professional Appointments

2009-present: Assistant of Physics of Metal Department, Department of Physics of Metals, Faculty of Physics, Ivan Franko National University, Lviv, Ukraine.

2008-2009: Assistant, Department of Informatics and Information Technologies in Internal Affairs, Lviv State University of Internal Affairs, Lviv, Ukraine.

2007-2008: Engineer, Department of Solid State Physics, Faculty of Physics, Ivan Franko National University, Lviv, Ukraine.

2005-2007: Post graduate student, Department of Physics of Metals, Faculty of Physics, Ivan Franko National University, Lviv, Ukraine.

2004-2005: Junior Research Fellow, Department of Physics of Metals, Faculty of Physics, Ivan Franko National University, Lviv, Ukraine.

2003-2004: Laboratory assistant, Department of Physics of Metals, Faculty of Physics, Ivan Franko National University, Lviv, Ukraine.

Publications Last 3 Years

1) Yakymovych, S. Mudry, Ch. Luef, H. Ipser, The competition between InBi- and In_2Bi-like atomic distributions before solidification. *Chem. Met. Alloys*, 1 (2008) 159-162.

2) V Sklyarchuk, Yu Plevachuk, S Mudry, A Yakymovych, U E Klotz and C Liu, Electrical conductivity of liquid Sn-Ti-Zr alloys. *J. Phys.: Conference Series*, 98 (2008) (062008).

3) S. Mudry, V. Sklyarchuk, A. Yakymovych, Viscosity of Bi-Ga liquid alloys. *J. Phys.: Conference Series*, 98 (2008) (062021).

4) S.Mudry, V. Sklyarchuk, A. Yakymovych, Influence of doping with Ni on viscosity of liquid Al. *J. phys. Stud.*, 12 (1) (2008) 1601-1605.

5) Yu. Plevachuk, V. Sklyarchuk, A. Yakymovych, S. Eckert, B. Willers, K. Eigenfeld, Density, viscosity and electrical conductivity of hypoeutectic Al-Cu liquid alloys. *Metall. Mater. Trans. A.*, 39(12) (2008) 3040-3045.

6) S. Mudry, V. Sklyarchuk, Yu. Plevachuk, A. Yakymovych, The viscosity of Bi-Zn liquid alloys. *J. Non-Cryst. Solids*, 354 (2008) 4415-4417

7) Yu. Plevachuk, V. Sklyarchuk, A. Yakymovych, G. Gerbeth, Microsegregation in liquid Pb-based eutectics. *J. Non-Cryst. Solids*, 354 (2008) 4443-4447.

8) V. Sklyarchuk, Yu. Plevachuk, A. Yakymovych, S. Eckert, G. Gerbert, K. Eigenfeld, Structure Sensitive Properties of liquid Al-Si alloys. *Int. J. Thermophys.*, 30 (2009) 1400-1410.

9) S. Mudry, A. Yakymovych, Viscosity of $In_{100-x}Sb_x$ molten alloys in the vicinity of equiatomic composition. *J. Mol. Liquids.*, 149 (2009) 105-107.

10) Yu. Plevachuk, S. Mudry, V. Sklyarchuk, A. Yakymovych, A. Korolyshyn, I. Shtablavyi, Yu. Kulyk, U. E. Klotz, Ch. Liu, Ch. Leinenbach, Determination of

liquidus temperature in Sn-Ti-Zr alloys by viscosity, electrical conductivity and XRD measurements. *Int. J. Mat. Res.*, 100(5) (2009) 689-694.

11) Yu. Plevachuk, V. Sklyarchuk, A. Yakymovych, P. Svec, D. Janickovic, E. Illekova, Electrical conductivity and viscosity of liquid Sn–Sb–Cu alloys. *J. Mat. Sci.: Mater. in Electronics.*, DOI: 10.1007/s10854-010-0188-6

12) Yakymovych, V. Sklyarchuk Yu. Plevachuk, S. Mudry, Viscosity and concentration fluctuations in liquid In-Sb and In-Bi alloys. *Rev. Adv. Mater. Sci.*, 23 (2010) 213-218.

13) S.I. Mudry, V.M. Sklyarchuk Yu.O. Plevachuk, A.S. Yakymovych, Viscosity of Sb-Sn melts. *Inorg. Mat.*, 46 (2010) 833-835.

In: Materials Science Researcher Biographical Sketches ...   ISBN: 978-1-61942-153-0
Editors: Satomi Matsumoto and Ueda Iwate   © 2013 Nova Science Publishers, Inc.

Chapter 22

BIOGRAPHICAL SKETCH

Linda Zou, Professor

Date of Birth: 22 July 1964

Education

Institution and Location	Degree	Year Conferred	Scientific Field
	PhD		Chem
	MEng		
	BEng		

Contact Points: 61 8 8302 5489

Research and Professional Experience

Associated Prof Linda Zou received her PhD in applied chemistry from Monash University (1998). Her main research contributions are in the fields of novel nanomaterials synthesis, including graphenes, ordered mesoporous carbons, visible light sensitive TiO_2/prorous adsorbent nano-composites, and in their application to solve "real world" problems, in water purification and desalination. In desalination research, Dr Zou has focused on low energy alternative desalination methods. Her contributions in developing novel carbons electrode materials in capacitive deionisation process, has achieved greatly improved electrode efficiency and is received recognition internationally. Her recent research work also include in hydrophilic surface modification of RO membranes to reduce biofouling. From 2000 until now, Professor Linda Zou has successfully received many national competitive Australian Research Council grants. She currently is the lead researchers of two Discovery grants, and three Linkage grants. Her research outcomes have been well published on peer reviewed international journals and she is a regular presenter at major IWA, IDA international water and desalination conferences. She is the main inventor of one international patent and two provisional patents, and has attracted substantial industry investment for commercialisation. Before joining UniSA in June 2008 as Research Associate Professor, Dr Linda Zou worked as lecture and then Senior in Environmental Engineering at Deakin University during 1999-2005. She then moved to Victoria as Research Associated Profess in 2006-2008.

Professional Appointments

November 2010-present: Professor, Deputy Director, SA Water Centre for Water Management and Reuse, UniSA

June 2008 - October 2010: Associate Professor and Deputy Director, SA Water Centre for Water Management and Reuse, UniSA

Jan 2006- May 2008: Associate Professor, Institute for Sustainability and Innovation, Victoria University

2004 - 2005: Senior Lecturer, School of Engineering and Technology, Deakin University

1999 - 2003: Lecturer, School of Engineering and Technology, Deakin University.

Publications during last three years

1. H. Li, L. Zou, L. Pan, Z. Sun "Novel graphene-like electrodes for capacitive deionization" Environmental Science & Technology, doi:10.1021/es101888j.
2. H, Li, W, Zhang, L. Zou, L. Pan and Z. Sun "An environmentally friendly approach to synthesis TiO2-graphene composites via visible light photocatalytic reduction of graphene oxide" Journal of Materials Research, Accepted for publication in August 2010.
3. Q. Shen, W. Zhang, Z. Hao and L. Zou 2010 "A Study on the Synergistic Adsorptive and Photocatalytic Activities of TiO2-xNx/Beta Composite Catalysts under Visible Light Irradiation", Chemical Engineering Journal, vol 165, pp301-309.
4. J. Xu, G. Ruan, L, Zou and C. Gao 2010 "Effect of chlorine and acid injectino on hollow fiber RO for SWRO" Desalination, vol 262, pp.115-120.
5. A. Rathinam and L. Zou 2010 "Biosorption of Bovine Serum Albumin by Ulva lactuca Biomass from Industrial Wastewater: Equilibrium, Kinetic and Thermodynamic Study" Journal of Hazardous Materials, doi:10.1016/j.jhazmat.2010.08.077.
6. H. Li, L. Zou, L. Pan and Z. Sun 2010 'Using graphene nano flakes as electrodes to remove ferric ions by capacitive deionization' Separation and Purification Technology Vol 75, pp8-14.
7. W. Zhang, L. Zou and L. Wang 2010 'Visible-light assisted methylene blue (MB) removal by novel TiO2/adsorbent nanocomposites' Water Science and Technology, vol 61, pp2863-2871.
8. B. Zhu, L. Zou, C. Doherty, A. J. Hill, Y. S. Lin, X. Hu, H. Wang and M. Duke 2010 'Investigation of the effects of ion and water interaction on structure and chemistry of silicalite MFI type zeolite for its potential use as a seawater desalination membrane' Journal of Materials Chemistry. Vol 20, pp4675-4683.
9. W. Zhang, L. Zou and L. Wang 2009 'Photocatalytic TiO2/adsorbent nanocomposites prepared via wet chemical impregnation for wastewater treatment: as review' Applied Catalysis A: General Vol 371 pp1-9.

10. H. Li, L. Pan, Y. Zhang, L. Zou, C. Sun, Y. Zhan and Z. Sun, 2010 'Kinetics and thermodynamics study for electrosorption of NaCl onto carbon nanotubes and carbon nanofibers electrodes' Chemical Physics Letters. Vol 480, pp161-166.

11. L. Zou, L. Li, Song and G. Morris 2010 'Improving the capacitive deionisation performance by optimising pore structures of the electrodes' Water Science and Technology, Vol 61.5 pp1227-1233.

12. L. Li, L. Zou, H Song and G Morris 2009 'Ordered mesoporous carbons synthesized by a modified sol-gel process for electrosorptive removal of sodium chloride' Carbon Vol 47 pp775-781.

13. B Zhu and L. Zou 2009 'Trapping and decomposing of colour compounds from recycled water by TiO2 coated activated carbon' Journal of Environmental Management, Vol 90 pp3217-3225.

14. X. D. Dai, L. Zou, Z. F. Yan and M. Milliken 2009 'Adsorption characteristics of N-nitrosodimethylamine from aqueous solution on surface-modified activated carbon. Journal of Hazardous Materials Vol 168 pp51-56.

15. B, Zhu and L. Zou 2009 'Removal of colour compounds from recycled water using combined activated carbon adsorption and AOP decomposition' Journal of Advanced Oxidation Technologies, Vol 12 No 1, pp47-54.

16. L. Li, L. Zou, H Song and G Morris 2009 'Ordered mesoporous carbons synthesized by a modified sol-gel process for electrosorptive removal of sodium chloride' Carbon Vol 47 pp775-781.

17. H. Tian, J. Li, L. Zou, Z. Mu and Z. Hao 2009 'Removal of DDT from aqueous solutions using mesoporous silica materials' Journal of Chemical Technology and Biotechnology. DOI 10.1002/jctb.2067.

18. L. Zou, P Sanciolo, G Leslie, 2008 'Using MF-NF-RO train to Produce Low Salt and High Nutrient Value Recycled Water for Agriculture Irrigation' Water Science and Technology Vol 58, pp1837-1840.

19. S. S. Tan, L. Zou, E. Hu, 2008 'Kinetic modeling for photosynthesis of hydrogen and methane through catalytic reduction of carbon dioxide with water vapour' Catalysis Today Vol 131 pp125-129.

20. P. Sanciolo, L. Zou, S. Gray, G. Leslie and D. Stevens, 2008 'Accelerated seeded precipitation pretreatment of municipal wastewater to reduce scaling' Chemophere Vol 72, pp243-249.

21. L. Zou, H. Song, L. Li and G. Morris 2008 'Using mesoporous carbon electrodes for water desalination' Water Research Vol 42, pp2340-2348.

22. L. Zou and B. Zhu, 2008. 'The synergistic effect of ozonation and photocatalysis on color removal from reused water' Journal of Photochemistry and Photobiology A: Chemistry Vol 196, pp24-32.

23. L. Zou, D. Qi and G. Morris 2008 'Low Cost Activated Carbon Electrosorptive Deionisation Technology in Brackish Water Desalination' Desalination Vol 225 pp329-340.

24. L. Zou and B. Zhu, 2007 'Enhancing the reuse of treated effluent by photo catalytic process' Journal of Advanced Oxidation Technologies Vol 10, No 2 pp273-281.

25. D. Qi, L. Zou and E. Hu, 2007 'Electrosorption; An alternative option for desalination' Research Journal of Chemistry and Environment Vol 11(3) pp92-95.

26. M. L. Ackland, L. Zou, D. Freestone, S. van de Waasenburg, A. A Michalczyk 2007 'Diesel exhaust particulate matter induces formation of multinucleate cells and apoptosis through a zinc transporter-dependent pathway in human airway cells'. Immunology and Cell Biology. 85 pp617-622.

27. L. Zou, Y. Luo and E. J. Hu 2007 'Using titania photocatalysts to degrade toluene in a combined adsorption and photocatalytic process' Journal of Advanced Oxidation technologies Vol 10 No1 pp31-36.

In: Materials Science Researcher Biographical Sketches ...   ISBN: 978-1-61942-153-0
Editors: Satomi Matsumoto and Ueda Iwate   © 2013 Nova Science Publishers, Inc.

Chapter 23

BIOGRAPHICAL SKETCH

Victor Evgen'evich Zubov

Affiliation: Faculty of Physics, M.V. Lomonosov Moscow State University

Date of Birth: 25.06.1946

Education

Institution and Location	Degree	Year Conferred	Scientific Field
Theme "Magnetooptical investigation of near-surface magnetic structures"; Faculty of Physics, M.V. Lomonosov Moscow State University.	Doctor of Sciences	1994	Physics and Mathematics
Theme "Surface magnetism of hematite", Faculty of Physics, M.V. Lomonosov Moscow State University.	Kandidat of Sciences	1976	Physics and Mathematics
M.V. Lomonosov Moscow State University,.Address: Faculty of Physics, MSU, Leninskie Gory, Moscow, 119991, Russia	Graduated from Faculty of Physics	1970	

Research and Professional Experience

Fields of scientific interests
low dimension magnetic structures (domain walls, Bloch lines, Bloch points), surface magnetism; Magnetooptical spectroscopy of ferrodielectrics; Magnetochemistry, influence of adsorption on magnetic properties of substances; Development of magnetooptical methods of investigation of magnetics.

The main achivements
For the first time surface magnetism on natural faces of weak ferromagnetic hematite and iron borate was observed by means of magnetooptical method. The theory of surface anisotropy and surface magnetism was developed. For the first time zero-dimensional magnetic substructural elemets of Bloch-point type were observed in the near-surface region of 180-degree domain wall in iron. It was established that coercive field of magnetic microstructural elements depended on its dimensionality. It has been shown that reversible adsorption-desorption processes proceeding through the formation of hydrogen bonds induce the perpendicular surface magnetic anisotropy in the amorphous ferromagnet.

Professional Appointments

Junior researcher, 1975-1982; Senior researcher, 1982-1995; Leading researcher, 1995-2000; Chief researcher from 2000 till date at Faculty of Physics, M.V. Lomonosov Moscow State University.

Honors

He was rewarded with the medal or the Ministry of Higher Education of the USSR for the best scientific work in 1983. In 1990 he got the first prize for the best experimental work on physics in the Moscow State University.

Publications during Last Three Years

V.E. Zubov, N.L. Levshin. Perpendicular surface magnetic anisotropy in an amorphous ferromagnet induced by adsorption occurring through the mechanism of the formation of hydrogen bonds. JETP Letters. 2009. Vol. 90, No 4, p. 268-271.

E.M. Maksimova, I.A. Nauhatsky, M.B. Strugatsky, V.E. Zubov. Surface magnetism of real iron borate monocrystals. J. Magn. Magn. Mater. 2010, Vol. 322, p. 477-480.

V.E. Zubov, A.D.Kudakov, N.L.Levsyin, N.A.Mezenkov. Domain Structure Reversible Reconstruction of Amorphous Ferromagnetic by Water Molecules Weak Adsorption. Solid State Phenomena (Magnetism and magnetic materials) 2009, Vol. 152-153, p. 428-430.

V.E. Zubov, A.D.Kudakov, M.Inoue, H.Uchida. Anomalously high surface deceleration of the domain wall and magnetic stray field micro-distribution over a surface of amorphous ferromagnet. J. Magn. Magn. Mater. 2010, Vol. 322, p. 7-11.

V.E. Zubov, A.D.Kudakov, N.L.Levsyin, M.Yu. Gusev, N.S. Neustroev. Reversible-adsorption-induced of domain width in iron garnet films. JETP Letters. 2011. Vol. 94, No 1, p. 45-47.

PART 2 – RESEARCH SUMMARIES

In: Materials Science Researcher Biographical Sketches ...   ISBN: 978-1-61942-153-0
Editors: Satomi Matsumoto and Ueda Iwate   © 2013 Nova Science Publishers, Inc.

Chapter 24

57FE MÖSSBAUER SPECTROSCOPIC AND DENSITY FUNCTIONAL THEORY (DFT) STUDY ON THE INTERACTIONS OF THE METAL ION WITH MONOSACCHARIDES

Yassin Jeilani, Beatriz H. Cardelino and Natarajan Ravi
Spelman College, Atlanta, GA, US

RESEARCH SUMMARY

The fundamental electrical and magnetic interactions between iron ions and biomaterials were investigated using an experimental approach, 57Fe Mössbauer spectroscopy, and ab initio computational methods. A conventional spin-Hamiltonian approach adopted for the data analysis of the Mössbauer data showed that the metal ion in the Fe-chitosan complex is in the high-spin ferric state and that it has an internal magnetic field of approximately 440 kG, at the nucleus. The magnitude of the internal field arises from the predominant Fermi-contact interaction of the high-spin ferric species with N/O ligands. This book proposes a scheme for the Fe-chitosan complex based on the analysis of the experimental data.

In: Materials Science Researcher Biographical Sketches …   ISBN: 978-1-61942-153-0
Editors: Satomi Matsumoto and Ueda Iwate   © 2013 Nova Science Publishers, Inc.

Chapter 25

ADVANCED ULTRASONIC CHARACTERIZATION OF FRESH CEMENTITOUS MATERIALS

D. G. Aggelis
University of Ioannina, Greece

RESEARCH SUMMARY

Concrete is the most widely used construction material due to low price, considerable load bearing capacity and the easiness to be formed in different shapes. If all standard procedures are followed and the concrete is made by the designed mix proportions, the possibility that it will not obtain the desired properties is highly unlikely. Therefore, quality characterization of concrete while it is still fresh is desirable. Concrete performance, including strength and durability, depends on the constituent material proportions. This book presents and discusses research on the quality characterization of the fresh material, which has been attempted by means of ultrasonic wave propagation. (Imprint: Novinka Books)

In: Materials Science Researcher Biographical Sketches ...   ISBN: 978-1-61942-153-0
Editors: Satomi Matsumoto and Ueda Iwate   © 2013 Nova Science Publishers, Inc.

Chapter 26

ADVANCES IN POLYMER NANOCOMPOSITE TECHNOLOGY

Vikas Mittal

Dept. of Chemistry and Applied Biosciences, Inst. of Chemical and Bioengineering, Zurich, Switzerland

RESEARCH SUMMARY

Polymer nanocomposites have revolutionized the research effort in the field of composites as they lead to the achievement of synergistic effects from the organic and inorganic components of the system and have led to the expansion of the spectrum of application of the commodity polymers to more advanced high end applications. Although a number of successful systems could be achieved, the inorganic filler still could not be optimally dispersed on nanometer scale in non polar polymers. Also, the thermal degradation of the surface modification of the inorganic component disturbs the organic inorganic phase compatibility and hence the resulting composite properties. In recent years, many new techniques have been employed to overcome these problems which include more advanced modification protocols of the inorganic filler, development of more thermally stable surface modification and altogether new synthesis technologies for polyolefin nanocomposites. There has also been a constant need to compare the composite properties with the property models and hence to be able to predict the properties of the similar systems in advance. However, until now, the conventional models developed for conventional micro composites were used, which in no way maps the nanocomposite systems. The recently developed statistical as well as finite element methods focusing the real nanocomposite morphologies have been more helpful for this purpose. Though a tremendous research focus lies on these polymer systems, there is also a need to give some attention to more environmentally friendly nanocomposite systems and to develop methods to achieve proper recycling.

In: Materials Science Researcher Biographical Sketches ...   ISBN: 978-1-61942-153-0
Editors: Satomi Matsumoto and Ueda Iwate   © 2013 Nova Science Publishers, Inc.

Chapter 27

AMINES GRAFTED CELLULOSE MATERIALS

Nadege Follain
Joseph Fourier University, Grenoble, France

RESEARCH SUMMARY

Native cellulose is a structural material that is biosynthesized as microfibrils by a number of living organisms ranging from higher and lower plants, to some ameobae, sea animals, bacteria and fungi. The chemical modification of cellulose microfibrils is investigated for preparing new bio-based materials with end-use properties in the fields of adhesion, textile, detergent, paint, cosmetic, medicine, food, etc. This book highlights the methods of preparing the cellulose conjugates which can be water-soluble materials or water-insoluble materials, to identify linkage with carboxylated cellulose materials through amide bonds and to understand the obtained results following by FT-IR, NMR spectroscopies (at liquid and solid states) and electron paramagnetic resonance spectroscopy.

In: Materials Science Researcher Biographical Sketches …   ISBN: 978-1-61942-153-0

Editors: Satomi Matsumoto and Ueda Iwate   © 2013 Nova Science Publishers, Inc.

Chapter 28

Asphalt Surfaces as Ecological Traps for Water-Seeking Polarotactic Insects: How Can the Polarized Light Pollution of Asphalt Surfaces Be Reduced?

Péter Malik, Ramón Hegedüs, György Kriska, Susanne Åkesson,
Bruce Robertson and Gábor Horváth

Eötvös University, Budapest, Hungary

Research Summary

The surface of dry or wet asphalt roads reflect partially linearly polarized light, the degree of linear polarization p of which depends on the darkness and roughness of asphalt: the darker and/or the smoother the asphalt, the higher the p of light reflected from it. If the asphalt is sunlit and the direction of view is parallel to the solar-antisolar meridian, then the direction of polarization of asphalt-reflected light is horizontal. In this case the asphalt surface can attract water-seeking aquatic insects, because they detect water by means of the horizontal polarization of light reflected from the water surface. This phenomenon is called positive polarotaxis. This new book proposes the use of these remedies on asphalt roads running near emergence sites of endangered aquatic insects, especially in the vicinity of wetlands, rivers and lakes.

In: Materials Science Researcher Biographical Sketches ...   ISBN: 978-1-61942-153-0

Editors: Satomi Matsumoto and Ueda Iwate   © 2013 Nova Science Publishers, Inc.

Chapter 29

BORATE-TELLURATE GLASSES: AN ALTERNATIVE OF IMMOBILIZATION OF THE HAZARDOUS WASTES

Simona Rada[1], Eugen Culea[1] and Monica Culea[2]
[1]Technical University of Cluj-Napoca, Romania and others
[2]Babes-Bolyai University, Cluj-Napoca, Romania

RESEARCH SUMMARY

Immobilization of high level toxic wastes by vitrification is a well established process that has been studied extensively over last 40 years. A suitable glass host is used to dissolve the high level nuclear waste to form a glassy (vitreous) homogeneous product that can be cast into suitable forms, including large glass blocks. The main advantages of the vitrification route include the fact glass is a good solvent for waste, glasses can be processed at reasonably low temperatures, glass is very tolerant of variations in waste composition, glass exhibits reasonable chemical durability, glass is radiation resistant and can accommodate changes occurring during decay of high level nuclear waste constituents. This new book analyzes the immobilization of high level toxic wastes through the use of an appropriate glass host.

In: Materials Science Researcher Biographical Sketches ...   ISBN: 978-1-61942-153-0
Editors: Satomi Matsumoto and Ueda Iwate   © 2013 Nova Science Publishers, Inc.

Chapter 30

CALIXARENE COMPLEXES WITH SOLVENT MOLECULES

O. V. Surov, M. I. Voronova and A. G. Zakharov
Russian Academy of Sciences, Ivanovo, Russia

RESEARCH SUMMARY

Solid calixarenes as receptors are characterized by phase transitions, which occur in binding of neutral molecules of guest compounds with the formation of clathrates or guest–host intercalation compounds. The process of clathrate formation in the binding of a guest by a host is accompanied by a significant rearrangement of the packing of host molecules, and the result of this rearrangement can depend considerably on the molecular structure of the guest. This new book presents and discusses research on the subject of solid-state complexation.

In: Materials Science Researcher Biographical Sketches ...   ISBN: 978-1-61942-153-0
Editors: Satomi Matsumoto and Ueda Iwate   © 2013 Nova Science Publishers, Inc.

Chapter 31

CHANNELING OF PROTONS THROUGH CARBON NANOTUBES

D. Borka, S. Petrović and N. Nešković

Vinèa Institute of Nuclear Sciences, Belgrade, Serbia

RESEARCH SUMMARY

This book contains a thorough theoretical consideration of the process of proton channeling through carbon nanotubes. A brief summary of the theoretical and experimental results of studying ion channeling through nanotubes is first discussed. Then, the process of ion channeling is described briefly. After that, the crystal rainbow effect is introduced. A description how it was discovered, and present the theory of crystal rainbows, as the proper theory of ion channeling in crystals and nanotubes is provided. It is shown that the evolution of the angular distribution of channeled protons with the nanotube length can be divided in the cycles defined by the rainbow effect.

In: Materials Science Researcher Biographical Sketches ...   ISBN: 978-1-61942-153-0
Editors: Satomi Matsumoto and Ueda Iwate   © 2013 Nova Science Publishers, Inc.

Chapter 32

CHARACTERIZATION OF ADVANCED STRUCTURAL MATERIALS BY ACOUSTIC EMISSION INDICES

D. G. Aggelis
University of Ioannina, Greece

RESEARCH SUMMARY

Highly demanding engineering applications demand advanced materials in terms of strength, toughness and durability. In order to characterize the performance of these materials, advanced monitoring methods are also sought for, which supply the necessary information about the structural integrity in a non-destructive way. One of the techniques applied for real time monitoring of the damage process is Acoustic Emission (AE). AE is based on the elastic waves which propagate mainly after crack propagation incidents. This book examines the Acoustic Emission technique, as well as the need for advanced materials.

In: Materials Science Researcher Biographical Sketches ...   ISBN: 978-1-61942-153-0
Editors: Satomi Matsumoto and Ueda Iwate   © 2013 Nova Science Publishers, Inc.

Chapter 33

CHEMISTRY OF PHENOLIC COMPOUNDS: STATE OF THE ART

Jubaraj Bikash Baruah

Indian Institute of Technology Guwahati, Assam, India

RESEARCH SUMMARY

Since the ancient days of research polyphenolic compounds have found a variety of use in medicinal chemistry and presently have found their applications in material research. There is a diverse interest in studying polyphenolic-based materials ranging from enzymes to plastic materials. However, there is no unified approach towards these studies to correlate structures with the different types of properties in order to implement such studies in applied engineering. This book presents a unified approach on synthetic and natural polyphenolic compounds in different forms and elaborate their properties with selective examples.

In: Materials Science Researcher Biographical Sketches …   ISBN: 978-1-61942-153-0
Editors: Satomi Matsumoto and Ueda Iwate   © 2013 Nova Science Publishers, Inc.

Chapter 34

CHITOSAN HYDROLYSIS BY NON-SPECIFIC ENZYMES

Wenshui Xia[1] and Ping Liu[2]
[1]State Key Laboratory of Food Science and Technology,
Jiangnan University, PR China
[2]Jiangsu Animal Husbandry and Veterinary College, Jiangsu, PR China

RESEARCH SUMMARY

The focus of this book is the characterizations and hydrolyzing mechanism of the non-specific enzymes toward chitosan choosing the three typical non-specific enzymes: cellulase, lipase and papain as objects. The authors studied the enzymatic characteristics, purification, product analysis, glycoside bond cleavage, active sites and gene cloning of these enzymes to expatiate their non-specific hydrolysis mechanism.

In: Materials Science Researcher Biographical Sketches ...   ISBN: 978-1-61942-153-0
Editors: Satomi Matsumoto and Ueda Iwate   © 2013 Nova Science Publishers, Inc.

Chapter 35

COMBUSTION SYNTHESIS
OF ADVANCED MATERIALS

B. B. Khina

Physico-Technical Institute, National Academy of Sciences of Belarus,
Minsk, Belarus

RESEARCH SUMMARY

The goal of this book is to describe basic approaches to modeling non-isothermal interaction kinetics during CS of advanced materials and reveal the existing controversies and apparent contradictions between different theories, on one hand, and between theory and experimental data, on the other hand, and to develop criteria for a transition from traditional solid-state diffusion-controlled phase formation kinetics (a "slow", quasi-equilibrium interaction pathway) to non-equilibrium, "fast" dissolution-precipitation route.

In: Materials Science Researcher Biographical Sketches …   ISBN: 978-1-61942-153-0
Editors: Satomi Matsumoto and Ueda Iwate   © 2013 Nova Science Publishers, Inc.

Chapter 36

CONSTRUCTION MATERIALS

Leonid Dvorkin[1], Sunny Nwaubani[2] and Oleg Dvorkin[1]

[1]Rivne, Ukraine
[2]Anglia Ruskin University, Essex, UK

RESEARCH SUMMARY

The modern building materials science, along with the constructional characteristics of materials, includes the theoretical concepts, allowing to predict properties of materials and to operate them actively. The theoretical concepts of construction materials science are based on the complex of the physical and chemical, geological-mineralogical and other sciences studying a structure and properties of material objects. Construction materials science is inseparably connected with technology of materials and products, methodology of their quality indicators and testing. This book discusses how scientific and technical progress actively affects the development of construction materials science.

In: Materials Science Researcher Biographical Sketches ...   ISBN: 978-1-61942-153-0
Editors: Satomi Matsumoto and Ueda Iwate   © 2013 Nova Science Publishers, Inc.

Chapter 37

DEFINITION OF CONSTANTS FOR PIEZOCERAMIC MATERIALS

Vladimir A. Akopyan, Arkady Soloviev, Ivan A. Parinov and Sergey N. Shevtsov

Southern Federal University, Rostov-on-Don, Russia

RESEARCH SUMMARY

This monograph consists of investigation results obtained on the new theoretically well-grounded method for the total set of the compatible material constants for different piezoceramics. With this aim, there were carried out theoretical and experimental analysis, and various oscillation modes of electroelastic bars and plates were identified. Moreover, the physical and geometrical restrictions on the sample form were stated by using modified method of definition of the piezomodule d_{33} in quasistatic regime. These limitations allowed the authors to calculate the valid values of d_{33} for various piezoceramic families. By this, the boundaries of application of the above methods are discussed in this book. The results of identification of the various oscillation modes for bars and plates, and also the method and algorithm of the definition of total set of compatible material constants may significantly help in the development of the computation methods for characteristics of piezocomposite materials for force piezoactuators. One of the approaches in order to achieve this aim consists of practice forms of maximum displacements that could be created by using the stiffness matrices of composite based on the calculation algorithm of total set of the compatible piezoceramic material constants. Moreover, above modified algorithm may be used for research and development of new composites, in particular polymer-composite materials. This book is addressed to students, post-graduate students and specialists, taking part in the development, preparation and researching new materials and devices on their base.

In: Materials Science Researcher Biographical Sketches ...   ISBN: 978-1-61942-153-0
Editors: Satomi Matsumoto and Ueda Iwate   © 2013 Nova Science Publishers, Inc.

Chapter 38

DENTAL COMPOSITES WITH NANO-SCALED FILLERS

Matthew J. Little and Hao Fong

South Dakota School of Mines and Technology, South Dakota, US

RESEARCH SUMMARY

Developed almost half a century ago, dental composites, consisting of a polymeric resin matrix and silanized glass or ceramic fillers, presented opportunities never before equaled in modern dentistry. Compared to dental amalgams, the composites possess better esthetic property, have fewer safety concerns, and show reasonably satisfactory clinical results. Consequently, the composites have been widely adopted by the dental profession as the restorative material of choice. This book presents research which states that innovative dental composites reinforced with nano-scaled fillers including polyhedral oligomeric silsesquioxane (POSS), fibrillar silicate, and electrospun glass nanofibers were prepared, characterized, and evaluated.

In: Materials Science Researcher Biographical Sketches ...   ISBN: 978-1-61942-153-0
Editors: Satomi Matsumoto and Ueda Iwate   © 2013 Nova Science Publishers, Inc.

Chapter 39

EDIBLE POLYSACCHARIDE FILMS AND COATINGS

Pau Talens and María José Fabra and Amparo Chiralt
Universidad Politécnica de Valencia, Valencia, Spain

RESEARCH SUMMARY

Regulating the mass transfer in food systems by edible films and coatings can increase food-product shelf life and food quality. Besides their barrier properties, edible films and coatings can act as carriers for functional food additives, antioxidants, antimicrobial agents and nutrients; and due to their biodegradability nature, could have an impact on overall packaging requirements. The objectives of this book are to review research on polysaccharide film-formation and characteristics, analyze mechanical and barrier properties of polysaccharide-based films, summarize applications of polysaccharide films in food products, and make conclusions as to the status of polysaccharide films and their future developmental direction.

In: Materials Science Researcher Biographical Sketches …   ISBN: 978-1-61942-153-0
Editors: Satomi Matsumoto and Ueda Iwate   © 2013 Nova Science Publishers, Inc.

Chapter 40

ENERGETICS AND PERCOLATION PROPERTIES OF HYDROPHOBIC NANOPOROUS MEDIA

V. D. Borman and V. N. Tronin
Moscow State University, Moscow, Russia

RESEARCH SUMMARY

Energetics of "nanoporous medium-nonwetting liquid" systems is one of the new directions in basic and applied research. In the simple model of a porous media in the form of cylindrical channels, this threshold pressure is described by the Laplace-Washburn equation, where is the surface energy of the liquid is the pore radius and the contact angle (for a nonwetting liquid). Among the systems under investigation are silochromes, zeolites with liquid metals, hydrophobized silica gels, and zeolites with water and aqueous solutions of organic compounds and salts. In recent years, hydrophobized nanoporous media have become available owing to the development of the method used for modifying the surface of nanoporous media. This new book reviews research on hydrophobic nanoporous media.

In: Materials Science Researcher Biographical Sketches ...   ISBN: 978-1-61942-153-0

Editors: Satomi Matsumoto and Ueda Iwate   © 2013 Nova Science Publishers, Inc.

Chapter 41

EXAMINATION OF UNTREATED AND TREATED PAINT SURFACES BY 3D-MEASUREMENT TECHNOLOGY

Paul-Bernhard Eipper

Alte Galerie am Landesmuseum Joanneum, Raubergasse, Graz, Austria

RESEARCH SUMMARY

Grime and dirt are hazards to oil-paint-surfaces. To remove these impurities, paintings are usually cleaned dry or wet with surfactants in aqueous medium. However, dry methods are not sufficient to completely clean the surfaces. Therefore modification of aqueous cleaning methods are necessary and include using mild non-ionic surfactants, thickening of the solutions used, reduction of contact humidity, and increasing temperature and pH. The authors of this book examine oil paint surfaces through the use of new 3D-Measurement Technology.

In: Materials Science Researcher Biographical Sketches ...   ISBN: 978-1-61942-153-0
Editors: Satomi Matsumoto and Ueda Iwate   © 2013 Nova Science Publishers, Inc.

Chapter 42

FATIGUE BEHAVIOR OF SHORT FIBRE COMPOSITES

Gangadhara Prusty
University of New South Wales, Sydney, Australia

RESEARCH SUMMARY

Fibre-reinforced composites have been used for more than 50 years and are still evolving in terms of material integrity, manufacturing process and its performance under adverse conditions. The advent of graphite fibres from polyacrylonitrile organic polymer has resulted in a high performance material, namely carbon based composites, performing better in every respect than glass fibre-reinforced plastic (GFRP). However, glass fibres are still in high demand in wide applications, where the cost takes precedence over performance. This book examines the complex issues surrounding the fatigue, fracture and durability of GFRP-CSM.

In: Materials Science Researcher Biographical Sketches …   ISBN: 978-1-61942-153-0
Editors: Satomi Matsumoto and Ueda Iwate   © 2013Nova Science Publishers, Inc.

Chapter 43

FATIGUE OF POLYMER MATRIX COMPOSITES AT ELEVATED TEMPERATURES

John Montesano, Zouheir Fawaz, Kamran Behdinan and Cheung Poon

Ryerson Universit, Toronto, ON, Canada

RESEARCH SUMMARY

In recent years, advanced composite materials have been frequently selected for aerospace applications due to their light weight and high strength. Polymer matrix composite (PMC) materials have also been increasingly considered for use in elevated temperature applications, such as supersonic vehicle airframes and propulsion system components. A new generation of high glass-transition temperature polymers has enabled this development to materialize. Clearly, there is a requirement to better understand the mechanical behaviour of this class of composite materials in order to achieve widespread acceptance in practical applications. This book presents and discusses the results and apparent shortcomings in studies of levels of fatigue in polymer matrix composites.

In: Materials Science Researcher Biographical Sketches ...   ISBN: 978-1-61942-153-0
Editors: Satomi Matsumoto and Ueda Iwate   © 2013 Nova Science Publishers, Inc.

Chapter 44

FOLDING/UNFOLDING KINETICS OF LATTICE PROTEINS BY APPLYING A SIMPLE STATISTICAL MECHANICAL MODEL FOR PROTEIN FOLDING

Hiroshi Wako and Haruo Abe
Waseda University, Tokyo, Japan

RESEARCH SUMMARY

The folding/unfolding kinetics of a three-dimensional lattice protein was studied using a simple statistical mechanical model for protein folding that was previously developed. The model considers the specificity of an amino acid sequence and the native structure of a given protein. The characteristic relaxation rate on the free energy surface was calculated starting from a completely unfolded structure (or native structure) that is assumed to associate with a folding rate (or an unfolding rate). To elucidate the roles of individual amino acid residues in protein folding/unfolding kinetics, the kinetic properties for all possible single amino acid substitutions of these proteins were calculated and their responses were examined. This book presents and discusses research results in the kinetics of protein folding/unfolding.

In: Materials Science Researcher Biographical Sketches …   ISBN: 978-1-61942-153-0
Editors: Satomi Matsumoto and Ueda Iwate   © 2013 Nova Science Publishers, Inc.

Chapter 45

LASER-ASSISTED DEPOSITION OF BORON NITRIDE THIN FILMS AND NANOTUBES

Armando Luches and Anna Paola Caricato
University of Salento, Italy

RESEARCH SUMMARY

Pulsed laser deposition (PLD) is at present one of the most interesting technique for thin film deposition. In the PLD process a film is formed by ablating a solid target with energetic laser pulses and collecting the material of interest on a substrate placed a few cm from the target. According to its ability to carry the stoichiometry from the target to the substrate and to its relatively high growth rate (~0.1 nm/pulse), PLD is an attractive technique for compound thin film deposition. This technique offers the possibility of depositing thin films on room-temperature or low-temperature substrates, due to the high energy of the species forming the laser plasma plume expanding from the target to the substrate. This book reviews research on the depositon of c-BN films by using PLD, ion-assisted PLD and other laser-assisted procedures.

In: Materials Science Researcher Biographical Sketches ...

Editors: Satomi Matsumoto and Ueda Iwate

ISBN: 978-1-61942-153-0

© 2013 Nova Science Publishers, Inc.

Chapter 46

MACHINING AND FORMING TECHNOLOGIES. VOLUME 1

J. Paulo Davim
University of Aveiro, Aveiro, Portugal

RESEARCH SUMMARY

Nowadays, machining is one of the most important of manufacturing processes in which a cutting tool or others techniques are used to remove excess material from a workpiece so that the remaining material is the desired part shape. Forming technologies includes a large group of manufacturing processes in which plastic deformation and others techniques are used to change the shape of worpieces. Machining and forming technologies can be applied to a wide variety of materials, namely, metals, polymers, ceramics, composites, biomaterials, nanomaterials. This book focuses on focuses on machining and forming technologies.

In: Materials Science Researcher Biographical Sketches …   ISBN: 978-1-61942-153-0
Editors: Satomi Matsumoto and Ueda Iwate   © 2013 Nova Science Publishers, Inc.

Chapter 47

MAGNETIC INTERACTIONS IN OXO-CARBOXYLATE BRIDGED GADOLINIUM (III) COMPLEXES*

Laura Cañadillas-Delgado, Óscar Fabelo,
Catalina Ruiz-Pérez and Joan Cano
Universidad de La Laguna, Spain, and others

RESEARCH SUMMARY

Magneto-structural studies on polynuclear complexes, aimed at understanding the structural and chemical factors that govern the exchange coupling between paramagnetic centers, are of continuing interest. One of the best illustrative examples corresponds to the di-μ-hydroxo-dicopper(II) complexes where the angle at the hydroxo bridge is the main factor governing the nature and magnitude of the intramolecular magnetic coupling. This book presents a systematic study of complex formation between gadolinium(III) and carboxylate-containing ligands which investigates the factors that govern the magnetic coupling in the digadolinium(III) units.

In: Materials Science Researcher Biographical Sketches ...   ISBN: 978-1-61942-153-0
Editors: Satomi Matsumoto and Ueda Iwate   © 2013 Nova Science Publishers, Inc.

Chapter 48

MANUFACTURING TECHNOLOGY RESEARCH. VOLUME 1

J. Paulo Davim and Mark. J. Jackson
University of Aveiro, Aveiro, Portugal

RESEARCH SUMMARY

Today, manufacturing technology is an interdisciplinary field involving the analysis of product design to assure manufacturability, the selection, specification, and optimization of the required equipment, tooling, processes and operations. Manufacturing technology is well established in a great number of industries such as aircraft, automotive, aerospace, machine tools, moulds and dies, product manufacturing, computers, electronics, semiconductor and communications, biomedical, etc. This book focuses on all materials, metals, plastics, ceramics, composites, and bio and nanomaterials as well as all manufacturing processes.

In: Materials Science Researcher Biographical Sketches …   ISBN: 978-1-61942-153-0
Editors: Satomi Matsumoto and Ueda Iwate   © 2013 Nova Science Publishers, Inc.

Chapter 49

NANOCOMPOSITE COATINGS

Mahmood Aliofkhazraei and Alireza Sabour Rouhaghdam

Tarbiat Modares University, Tehran, Iran

RESEARCH SUMMARY

This book reviews research activities around fabrication of these kinds of two dimensional nanostructured coatings with examples of enhanced mechanical properties, corrosion resistance, and physical characteristics. As one of the useful and simple methods for fabrication of nanocomposite coatings, electrochemical deposition (electroplating) techniques are a strong focus in this book. The relation among nanotechnology and these kinds of nanostructures that come from "size effect" and "distribution effect" is discussed through different chapters of this book. Nanocomposite coatings have numerous advantages.

In: Materials Science Researcher Biographical Sketches ...   ISBN: 978-1-61942-153-0
Editors: Satomi Matsumoto and Ueda Iwate   © 2013 Nova Science Publishers, Inc.

Chapter 50

OPTIMIZATION IN POLYMER PROCESSING

António Gaspar-Cunha and José António Covas
University of Minho, Portugal

RESEARCH SUMMARY

Plastics processing is a major industrial activity, which yields components and systems for a wide range of industries, such as packaging, automotive, aeronautics, electrical and electronic, sports and leisure, toys, civil and construction, and agriculture. Most plastic components are manufactured either by extrusion or injection molding, but other techniques such as blow molding and thermoforming are also important. The productivity of these technologies is dictated by the equipment design, choice of the operating conditions and physical properties of the polymer system. This book discusses the recent scientific developments on the optimization of manufacturing engineering problems and applies them to polymer processing technologies.

In: Materials Science Researcher Biographical Sketches ...   ISBN: 978-1-61942-153-0

Editors: Satomi Matsumoto and Ueda Iwate   © 2013 Nova Science Publishers, Inc.

Chapter 51

PHASE FORMATION AND SUPERCONDUCTIVITY IN COPPER OXIDE BASED YBCO AND RU-1212 AND RU-1222 SYSTEMS PREPARED BY SOL-GEL AND COPRECIPITATION TECHNIQUES

Yeoh Lee Moi

Nilai University College, Malaysia

RESEARCH SUMMARY

The discovery of superconductivity behavior in ceramic materials based on copper oxide suggests that ceramic can be used as an insulator material. However, superconductivity mechanism-based copper oxides are still seen as mysterious and misunderstood by scientists, even though the search for materials with higher critical temperatures has been ongoing. This effort can be seen from the first discovery of superconductor in the critical temperature of mercury 4.2 K up to the highest critical temperature of 164 K in the copper oxide superconductors Hg-Ba-Ca-Cu-O in 1993. This book discusses the development of high temperature superconductors since the discovery of the first superconductor until now, as well as the basic properties of high temperature superconductor. In addition, it also describes various wet chemical methods in superconductors preparation.

In: Materials Science Researcher Biographical Sketches …   ISBN: 978-1-61942-153-0
Editors: Satomi Matsumoto and Ueda Iwate   © 2013 Nova Science Publishers, Inc.

Chapter 52

POLYFUNCTIONAL STABILIZERS OF POLYMERS

N. A. Mukmeneva, S. V. Bukharov, G. N. Nugumanova and A. M. Kochnev

Kazan State Technological Univ., Tatarstan, Russia

RESEARCH SUMMARY

The monograph is of interest to scientists specializing in physical chemistry. The results of research of polyfunctional stabilizers from the point of view of correlation of structure, reactivity and inhibiting efficiency on the basis of general kinetic approach and modern physical, chemical and mathematical methods of identification of mechanisms of their stabilizing action, both in modelling liquid-phase systems and solid polymers and their melts are analyzed. The method of the comparative estimation of inhibiting properties of the polyfunctional compounds based on semiempirical correlations "structure - properties" are considered.

Aspects of chemistry of high-molecular compounds include the results of research of polymer analogous reactions of polyfunctional stabilizers with liable groups, contained in the composition of polymers at various stages of their ageing. In the final chapters of the monograph the data on ageing and stabilization of various types of polymers (PO, PVC, heterogeneous chain polymers, rubbers, etc.) are considered, some variants of practical realization of intramolecular and mix synergism of antioxidizing action of polyfunctional stabilizers in polymers are presented.

In whole, the book represents the scientific work devoted to the subject of the development of polyfunctional stabilizers, in this work some aspects of organic chemistry, physical chemistry, chemistry of high-molecular compounds, issues of ageing and stabilization of polymers, practical forecasts for the usage of polyfunctional stabilizers are considered. The above said predetermines the importance of the monograph.

In: Materials Science Researcher Biographical Sketches …   ISBN: 978-1-61942-153-0
Editors: Satomi Matsumoto and Ueda Iwate   © 2013 Nova Science Publishers, Inc.

Chapter 53

SILICON CARBIDE PARTICULATE REINFORCED ALUMINUM ALLOYS MATRIX COMPOSITES FABRICATED BY SQUEEZE CASTING METHOD

Adem Onat
Sakarya University, Sakarya, Turkey

RESEARCH SUMMARY

Metal Matrix Composites (MMCs) are now attracting enormous interest, because of their superiority in strength, stiffness, wear resistance, elevated temperature strength or other engineering properties. Parallel to commercialisation, there are research centres throughout the world that are actively researching further development and exploitation of net or near net shape fabrication process. In this book, the production and characterisation of SiC particles reinforced Al alloy matrix composites produced by squeeze casting are investigated. The effects of volume fraction of SiC on microstructure, mechanical properties are examined as well. Also the results of the production of gravity cast matrix alloy, to determine the effect of pressure on microstructure and properties are described in this book.

In: Materials Science Researcher Biographical Sketches …   ISBN: 978-1-61942-153-0
Editors: Satomi Matsumoto and Ueda Iwate   © 2013 Nova Science Publishers, Inc.

Chapter 54

SMART FUNCTIONALLY GRADED PLATES: VIBRATION ANALYSIS OF FGM PLATES COUPLED WITH PIEZOELECTRIC LAYERS

Farzad Ebrahimi
University of Tehran, Iran

RESEARCH SUMMARY

The laminated composite structures can be tailored to design advanced structures, but the sharp change in the properties of each layer at the interface between two adjacent layers causes large inter-laminar shear stresses that may eventually give rise to well known phenomenon known as delamination. Such detrimental effects can be mitigated by grading the properties in a continuous manner across the thickness direction resulting in a new class of materials known as 'functionally graded materials' (FGMs). This book presents a non-linear dynamics and vibration analysis on functionally graded circular and annular plates that are bonded with piezoelectric actuator layers considering the implications of thermal effects on piezoelectric behavior of the coupled structure.

In: Materials Science Researcher Biographical Sketches …   ISBN: 978-1-61942-153-0
Editors: Satomi Matsumoto and Ueda Iwate   © 2013 Nova Science Publishers, Inc.

Chapter 55

STRUCTURE AND PROPERTIES OF MODIFIED POLYURETHANES

L. A. Sukhareva, O. A. Legonkova, E. I. Mzhachikh and V. N. Ivanova

Moscow State University of Applied Biotechnology, Russia

RESEARCH SUMMARY

Recently there has been a significant increase in the share of polyurethane varnish-and-paint materials in the total amount of varnish-and-paint materials produced in this country and abroad. Polyurethane coatings are used for protection of metal, concrete, re-inforced concrete, and wood; as well as in production of non-woven, doubled and combined fabrics for various purposes, in particular for footwear, clothing, technical fabrics and other articles. A characteristic feature of polyurethane coatings is also that they are used not only to produce coatings on traditional rigid supports but also on flexible porous supports. This book presents and reviews research on the structure and properties of modified polyurethanes.

In: Materials Science Researcher Biographical Sketches ...   ISBN: 978-1-61942-153-0
Editors: Satomi Matsumoto and Ueda Iwate   © 2013 Nova Science Publishers, Inc.

Chapter 56

SYNTHESIS, STRUCTURAL AND SPECTROSCOPIC PROPERTIES OF SOME NEW ERBIUM-BASED MATERIALS

Hassane Assaaoudi and Ian S. Butler
McGill University, Montreal, QC, Canada
Janusz A. Kozinski University of Saskatchewan, Saskatoon, Canada

RESEARCH SUMMARY

In recent years, particular attention has been devoted to developing "soft" chemistry approaches towards the synthesis of new lanthanide (rare-earth) materials under ambient conditions. This book presents a simple hydrothermal synthetic approach to produce a number of new erbium-based materials in the form of crystalline microflowers, hexagonal microlayers, microsticks and microspheres, which are comprised of nanoparticles, as well as nanofibers, nanorods and nanolayers. This book also discusses recent results concerning the synthesis, phases changes and vibrational spectra of rare-earth orthophosphates, together with similar data for the diphosphate, $ErKP_2O_7.2H_2O$, and the tricyclophosphate, $ErNa_3(P_3O_9)_2.9H_2O$

In: Materials Science Researcher Biographical Sketches ...   ISBN: 978-1-61942-153-0
Editors: Satomi Matsumoto and Ueda Iwate   © 2013 Nova Science Publishers, Inc.

Chapter 57

THE POTENTIAL FOR COST AND WEIGHT REDUCTION IN TRANSPORT APPLICATIONS THROUGH THE USE OF HEAT TREATED ALUMINUM HIGH PRESSURE DIECASTINGS

R. N. Lumley

CSIRO Light Metals Flagship, Melbourne, Australia

RESEARCH SUMMARY

High pressure diecasting (HPDC), in which molten metal is injected at high velocity into a die cavity, now accounts for over half of all aluminium castings worldwide. This manufacturing process has proved particularly suitable for the mass production of components, notably those with complex shapes. Due to the low costs associated with mass production, HPDC is also favored for use in the transport sector. This book gives an overview of the new technology and presents analyses for cases where substantial cost savings and weight reductions appear possible.

In: Materials Science Researcher Biographical Sketches ...   ISBN: 978-1-61942-153-0
Editors: Satomi Matsumoto and Ueda Iwate   © 2013 Nova Science Publishers, Inc.

Chapter 58

THE PROMOTING EFFECT OF LANTHANUM IN HETEROGENEOUS CATALYSTS

Maria do Carmo Rangel, Manuela de Santana Santos and Sergio Gustavo Marchetti

Universidade Federal da Bahia, Federação, Bahia, Brazil

RESEARCH SUMMARY

The interest for studying lanthanum compounds has been growing in recent years due to their attractive properties for industrial and technological purposes. Several applications in different fields have been discovered, such as components in various optical, electrical and magnetic applications, as well as catalytic materials. In this case, they are widely used as catalysts, supports and dopants. As a dopant, lanthanum is often used for stabilizing the gamma phase of alumina, in catalysts designed for high temperature applications, such as in automotive three-way catalytic process, in combustion for gas turbines and boilers and in hydrocarbon reforming. This book discusses how lanthanum is a very promising dopant for heterogeneous catalysts of different applications.

In: Materials Science Researcher Biographical Sketches ...   ISBN: 978-1-61942-153-0
Editors: Satomi Matsumoto and Ueda Iwate   © 2013 Nova Science Publishers, Inc.

Chapter 59

TREATMENT OF CHROMIUM CONTAMINATION IN THE ENVIRONMENT

Paitip Thiravetyan and Parinda Suksabye

King Mongkut's University of Technology Thonburi, Thakham, Bangkhuntien,
Bangkok, Thailand

RESEARCH SUMMARY

Chromium exits in the environment in trivalent Cr(III) and hexavalent Cr(VI) oxidation states. Cr(VI) is approximately 10 to 100 times more toxic than Cr (III) because its oxidizing potential is high and it easily penetrates biological membranes. In addition, Cr(VI) leads to liver damage, pulmonary congestion and causes skin irritation resulting in ulcer formation. Furthermore, a high Cr(VI) concentration is related to abnormal enzyme activities, altered blood chemistry, lowered resistance to pathogenic organisms, behavioral modifications, disrupted feeding, histopathology and hormo-regularatory upset. This book provides information regarding the treatment of Chromium contamination in our present environment.

In: Materials Science Researcher Biographical Sketches ...   ISBN: 978-1-61942-153-0
Editors: Satomi Matsumoto and Ueda Iwate   © 2013 Nova Science Publishers, Inc.

Chapter 60

NORLAND OPTICAL ADHESIVE AND LIQUID CRYSTAL COMPOSITE MATERIALS

Réda Benmouna and Mustapha Benmouna*

University Aboubekr Belkaïd, Faculty of Sciences,
Department of Physics, Tlemcen, Algeria

RESEARCH SUMMARY

This chapter reviews properties and applications of composite materials made of Norland Optical Adhesive and liquid crystal materials. The polymer support exhibits the texture of a film with Swiss cheese morphology and microscopic inclusions filled with small functional liquid crystal molecules. Under certain conditions of preparation, these systems have a grating morphology with a succession of liquid crystal and polymer shells. Systems with Swiss cheese morphology and mean diameter of inclusions in the micrometer range are strong scatterers of visible light and their applications are mainly in technologies using commutable windows and display devices. Other applications are also possible in multiplexing devices and routing of telecommunication signals provided that the nature of constituents in the initial mixture and the method of preparation are properly chosen. In general, one seeks liquid crystal domains with sizes in the nanometer range either with randomly distributed inclusions or using grating morphology. This study presents a state of the art of the properties of such composite materials encompassing morphology, phase behavior, thermo-mechanical and visco-elasticity aspects. Optical and electro-optical responses which are the basis for numerous applications are also examined. Both theoretical models and experimental investigations will be considered with a special reference to the work with which the authors are most familiar. A correlative analysis in made to demonstrate the relationship between composition of the initial mixture, conditions and methods of preparation and final properties of the materials.

---

* E-mail: redabenmouna@yahoo.com.

In: Materials Science Researcher Biographical Sketches ...   ISBN: 978-1-61942-153-0

Editors: Satomi Matsumoto and Ueda Iwate   © 2013 Nova Science Publishers, Inc.

Chapter 61

ENVIRONMENTAL AND CHEMICAL DEGRADATION OF BONDED POLYMERIC COMPOSITE JOINTS

Valeria La Saponara[*,1], *Richard A. Campbell*[2], *Patrick Sullivan*[3] *and Douglas Dierdorf*[2]

[1]Mechanical and Aerospace Engineering, University of California, Davis, CA, US

[2]Applied Research Associates, Tyndall AFB, FL, US

[3]Air Force Research Laboratory, Tyndall AFB, FL, US

RESEARCH SUMMARY

Bonded joints made with polymeric matrix composites are commonly adopted in structural applications where weight is a critical design parameter. They are also key elements in the repair and retrofitting of damaged structures, e.g. aircraft composite skin and reinforced concrete bridge columns. Advances in the design and inspection of bonded polymeric composite joints will therefore improve joints durability, and consequently the safety of composite structures, in a wide range of applications (aerospace, civil, ship, transportation and wind power engineering).

The scope of this chapter is to discuss one aspect of joint durability: chemical and mechanical degradation of the individual components of a typical aerospace joint, i.e. structural epoxy-based adhesive and carbon/epoxy. In a recent research project, these materials were separately exposed to an aggressive environment, consisting of full immersion in water or anti-icing additive (also called fuel additive) or jet fuel or hydraulic fluid. There were simplified laboratory testing conditions: no coatings, no mixing of fluids (i.e. jet fuel and anti-icing additive), no prior thermo-mechanical damage. Gravimetric data, hardness tests and microscopy support the presence of chemical degradation in the adhesive. The use of simple Fickian and non-Fickian two-stage sorption Langmuir models for gravimetric data appears successful for the results of some treatments, e.g. sorption of fuel additive by adhesive. This finding could be used for the purpose of multiphysics modeling of thermo-

* Corresponding author. E-mail vlasaponara@ucdavis.edu, phone +1-530-754-8938.

mechanical degradation of bonded joints. Finally, chemical degradation distinctly appears through Differential Scanning Calorimetry (DSC) and thermogravimetric (TGA) tests: significant changes were encountered when the adhesive was treated in anti-icing additive or hydraulic fluid, while other treatments seem to be much less detrimental for the adhesive. Carbon/epoxy, on the other hand, is impacted at a much lesser rate by fuel additive.

In: Materials Science Researcher Biographical Sketches ...   ISBN: 978-1-61942-153-0
Editors: Satomi Matsumoto and Ueda Iwate   © 2013 Nova Science Publishers, Inc.

Chapter 62

PULSED HIGH- AND LOW-ENERGETIC FILM GROWTH ON THERMOPLASTIC POLYURETHANE BY PULSED LASER DEPOSITION AT ROOM TEMPERATURE

J. M. Lackner[1,], W. Waldhauser[1], R. Major[2] and B. Major[2]*

[1]Joanneum Research Forschungsgesellschaft mbH, Institute of Surface Technologies and Photonics, Niklasdorf, Austria

[2]Polish Academy of Sciences, Institute of Metallurgy and Materials Sciences, Krakow, Poland

RESEARCH SUMMARY

The coating of polymer materials by protecting and functional films requires high efforts in the development of coating techniques due to the very different mechanical and thermal properties of polymer substrates and metal or ceramic films. The film has to fulfil both high adhesion and optimized microstructure to prevent failing in its application. The current work describes a new vacuum coating technique for polymer materials with inorganic films – the Pulsed Laser Deposition (PLD) process, characterized by a high-energetic pulsed plasma and the easy possibility to room temperature deposition (RT-PLD). Thus, pseudodiffusion interfaces were found due to the high-energetic particle bombardment during PLD coating. Additionally, changes of the polyurethane chemical binding are evident, like the transition from C=O to C–O–R binding, in which titanium atoms could act as new binding partners to the O species. Although very high film adhesion can be guaranteed in the PLD by the formation of pseudodiffusion interfaces, preventing the well-known buckling phenomenon, high film stresses result in plastic deformation of the soft polymer surface and the formation of wrinkles. The reasons and effects of wrinkling – even starting in growing films – on the

---

[*] Joanneum Research Forschungsgesellschaft mbH, Institute of Surface Technologies and Photonics, Leobner Strasse 94, A-8712 Niklasdorf, Austria,Tel.: +43 316 876 2305, Fax: +43 316 876 2310, Email: juergen.lackner@joanneum.at.

film behaviour are described in this work, based on both practical investigations, using transmission electron microscopy, X-ray diffraction and atomic force microscopy, and theoretical finite element modelling.

In: Materials Science Researcher Biographical Sketches …   ISBN: 978-1-61942-153-0
Editors: Satomi Matsumoto and Ueda Iwate   © 2013 Nova Science Publishers, Inc.

Chapter 63

ADHESIVE BONDING OF HYDRO-THERMALLY MODIFIED WOOD

*Andreja Kutnar**

University of Primorska,
Primorska Institute for Natural Sciences and Technology, Koper, Slovenia;
ILTRA d.o.o., Ljubljana, Slovenia

RESEARCH SUMMARY

In the past years considerable increase in the hydrothermal modification of wood was observed. Mostly the heat treatments are performed to change the hygroscopicity of wood. Furthermore, densification processes are utilizing the hydrothermal treatments. A key factor in the efficient utilization of timber resources is the adhesive bonding of wood, since manufacturing of wood based composites depends on forming bonds between individual wooden elements. Wood-based composites offer several advantages over sawn wood, such as the utilization of waste material, better distribution of non-homogeneities, and control of the product properties in the manufacturing process. Therefore the efficient utilization of hydro-thermally modified wood depends on its adhesive potential. The combined effects of temperature and moisture modify the properties of the polymeric components of wood and its porous structure. Wood tissue is exposed to high temperatures that can cause surface inactivation. Hydrothermal treatment could reduce the surface free energy and thus result in the poorer wettability of the modified wood surface. Furthermore, penetration and spreading of the resin could be influenced by hydrothermal treatment. In spite of numerous studies of hydro-thermally modified wood, the adhesion potential of hydro-thermal treated wood has not been studied extensively in the past. The aim of this chapter is to provide literature review of aspects like surface properties of hydro-thermally modified wood related to bondability, wetting, and penetration. Finally, future directions regarding efficient application of hydro-thermally modified wood including densified wood in polymer composites are discussed.

---

* E-mail address: andreja.kutnar@upr.si.

In: Materials Science Researcher Biographical Sketches ...   ISBN: 978-1-61942-153-0
Editors: Satomi Matsumoto and Ueda Iwate   © 2013 Nova Science Publishers, Inc.

Chapter 64

THE USE OF ADHESIVE FILMS IN TRANSDERMAL AND MUCOADHESIVE DOSAGE FORMS

Kalliopi Dodou
Sunderland Pharmacy School,
University of Sunderland, UK

RESEARCH SUMMARY

Thin polymeric films with adhesive ability are useful for transdermal and mucoadhesive drug delivery systems. Polymer materials with adhesive ability in their dry state are integral to the formulation of patch systems for topical and transdermal drug delivery. Such polymers are often called "pressure sensitive adhesives" due to their capacity to attach to the skin surface with the application of light pressure. In the drug-in-adhesive design the drug is mixed with the adhesive polymer to produce a thin medicated film. The adhesive performance of these films can be monitored directly using tack and peel tests and indirectly by correlation with rheological parameters. Polymers with adhesive ability following absorption of moisture are useful in the formulation of mucoadhesive films for transmucosal (*e.g.* buccal, nasal, ocular) drug delivery. Such polymers are hydrophilic (hydrogels). Following hydration, polymer chains relax and interact with mucus glucoprotein chains, primarily by hydrogen bonding. This chapter will describe the properties of the adhesive polymers used in the design of transdermal and mucoadhesive films, the mechanism of adhesion and the tests that can be applied to monitor the adhesive performance.

In: Materials Science Researcher Biographical Sketches ...   ISBN: 978-1-61942-153-0

Editors: Satomi Matsumoto and Ueda Iwate   © 2013 Nova Science Publishers, Inc.

Chapter 65

MODELLING ADHESION BY ASYMPTOTIC TECHNIQUES

F. Lebon and R. Rizzoni
Aix-Marseille University, Marseille, France

RESEARCH SUMMARY

In this chapter, a review of theoretical and numerical asymptotic studies on thin adhesive layers is proposed. A general mathematical method is presented for mod- elling the mechanical behavior of bonding and interfaces. This method is based on a simple idea that the adhesive film is supposed to be very thin; the mechanical problem depends strongly on the thinness of the adhesive. It is quite natural, mathematically and mechanically, to consider the limit problem, that is, the asymptotic problem ob- tained when the thickness and, possibly, the mechanical characteristics of the adhesive thin layer tend to zero. This asymptotic analysis leads to a limit problem with a me- chanical constraint on the surface, to which the layer shrinks. The formulation of the limit problem includes the mechanical and geometrical properties of the layer. This limit problem is usually easier to solve numerically by using finite elements software. Theoretical results (i.e. limit problems) can be usually obtained by using at least four mathematical techniques: gamma-convergence, variational analysis, asymptotic ex- pansions and numerical studies. In the chapter, some examples will be presented: comparable rigidity between the adhesive and the adherents, soft interfaces, adhesive governed by a non convex energy and imperfect adhesion between adhesive and ad- herents. Some numerical examples will also be given and, finally, an example of a numerical algorithm will be presented.

In: Materials Science Researcher Biographical Sketches …   ISBN: 978-1-61942-153-0
Editors: Satomi Matsumoto and Ueda Iwate   © 2013 Nova Science Publishers, Inc.

Chapter 66

DURABILITY OF ADHESIVES AND MATRICES FOR POLYMER COMPOSITES USED IN RESTORATION AND REHABILITATION OF BUILDING STRUCTURES UNDER NATURAL AND ACCELERATED WEATHERING CONDITIONS[*]

Mariaenrica Frigione[†]
Department of Engineering for Innovation,
University of Salento, Lecce, Italy

RESEARCH SUMMARY

The success of the fiber-reinforced polymer (FRP) systems in the restoration and rehabilitation of civil and monumental structures is due to their excellent properties, generally superior than those of traditional building materials. Of great importance, however, is the behavior of the repaired structure under loading and its durability in the outside climate. The lack of specific standards for durability investigation of materials employed in such applications makes difficult the assessment of reliable theoretical models. As an example, the available standard tests for adhesives generally refer to resins cured at elevated temperatures, neglecting the peculiarities of "cold-cured" adhesives.

In this chapter, the durability of the base components of FRP specifically designed for civil engineering industry, is reviewed. The most common environmental agents, mostly responsible for the deterioration of the materials performance, are examined. Finally, standardized accelerating tests are discussed as an effective method to predict the long term behavior of the weathered materials.

---

[*] A version of this chapter also appears in *Encyclopedia of Polymer Composites: Properties, Performance and Applications*, published by Nova Science Publishers, Inc. It was submitted for appropriate modifications in an effort to encourage wider dissemination of research.

[†] Corresponding author: mariaenrica.frigione@unisalento.it.

In: Materials Science Researcher Biographical Sketches ...   ISBN: 978-1-61942-153-0
Editors: Satomi Matsumoto and Ueda Iwate   © 2013 Nova Science Publishers, Inc.

Chapter 67

REPLACING OF SYNTHETIC ADHESIVES WITH NATURAL ADHESIVES†

*Md. Moniruzzaman Khan and M. Rafiqul Islam**
Department of Civil and Resource Engineering, Dalhousie University,
Barrington Street, Halifax, Canada

RESEARCH SUMMARY

Adhesives or bonding agents surround all living beings in Nature and in their daily lives. Adhesives or bonding agents are used in a variety of industries: construction, packaging, furniture, automotive, appliance, textile, aircraft, and many others. However, most of them are toxic for human beings due to the presence of harmful synthetic additives. The long-term exposure to these toxic substances can cause a range of ailments, including cancer, asthma, and Alzheimer disease. The ultimate solution of this trend lies in the emulation of Nature following the true pathway of natural process. In this paper, a number of adhesives have been formulated from natural additives, which can lead us towards sustainable lifestyles. Experiments show that the product exhibit durability and strength comparable to commercially available products, while the required concentration of the adhesive is low. Further experiments indicate that alternative adhesives that are of organic origin can eliminate the use of synthetic adhesives entirely. Similarly, as a natural alternative to Plaster of Paris is proposed. This product has features very similar to the commercial Plaster of Paris. This product and others can become useful for people with chemical sensitivity, particularly the children and the elderly. This paper describes in detail the specific recommendations on natural adhesives, their strengths and durability as a function of temperature.

---

† A version of this chapter also appears in *Journal of Characterization and Development of Novel Materials*, Volume 1, Number 2, published by Nova Science Publishers, Inc. It was submitted for appropriate modifications in an effort to encourage wider dissemination of research.
* Corresponding author: E-mail: rafiqul.islam@dal.ca.

In: Materials Science Researcher Biographical Sketches …   ISBN: 978-1-61942-153-0
Editors: Satomi Matsumoto and Ueda Iwate   © 2013 Nova Science Publishers, Inc.

Chapter 68

THE HIGH VELOCITY IMPACT OF CARBON-FIBRE BASED COMPOSITE MATERIALS

P. J. Hazell and G. Appleby-Thomas*
Cranfield Defence and Security, Cranfield University,
Shrivenham, Swindon, Wiltshire, UK

RESEARCH SUMMARY

Carbon-fibre reinforced-plastic (CFRP) materials are becoming increasingly popular for their use in the design of aerospace structures due to their high stiffness and low density. Such structures can be susceptible to high velocity impacts. For example, the terrorist threat to civilian airliners in recent years has become all the more problematic due to the proliferation of MANPADS (man-portable air-defence systems). These systems are capable of launching a missile in the general direction of the aircraft and detonating a fragmenting munition at close proximity to an aircraft's structure, propelling a number of high velocity projectiles towards it. Equally, carbon-fibre based materials are also used extensively in spacecraft design. These structures are susceptible to hypervelocity impacts where the projectile strikes the structure at many kilometres-per-second. With greater number of aerospace structures being made from carbon-fibre based materials it is perhaps timely to assemble together the current research relevant to the high velocity impact of these materials.

---
* Email: p.j.hazell@cranfield.ac.uk; Tel: +44 (0) 1793 785731.

In: Materials Science Researcher Biographical Sketches ...   ISBN: 978-1-61942-153-0
Editors: Satomi Matsumoto and Ueda Iwate   © 2013 Nova Science Publishers, Inc.

Chapter 69

PROGRESS IN ORGANIC SPINTRONICS

Junfeng Ren[1,2], Guichao Hu[1,2], Yubin Zhang[2], Jie Lei[2], Hong Jiang[2] and Shijie Xie[,2]*

[1]College of Physics and Electronics, Shandong Normal University, Jinan, China
[2]School of Physics, State Key Laboratory of Crystal Materials,
Shandong University, Jinan, China

RESEARCH SUMMARY

Spintronics, or spin electronics, involves the investigation on active control and manipulation of spin degrees of freedom in solid-state systems. Both the experimental (Dediu 2002, Xiong 2004) and theoretical (Xie 2003) works reveal the possibility of spin injection and transport in organic materials. The combination of organic materials with spintronics-'organic spintronics' is an interesting topic for chemical as well as physical researchers. The progress in this area including our recent work is presented in this article. Three parts are considered: first the introduction of spintronics and organic materials, second the description of organic spintronics and the last a simple review of our recent investigation.

---
[*] E-mail address: xsj@sdu.edu.cn (S. Xie). Tel.: +86 531 88377035×8321. (Corresponding author).

In: Materials Science Researcher Biographical Sketches …   ISBN: 978-1-61942-153-0
Editors: Satomi Matsumoto and Ueda Iwate   © 2013 Nova Science Publishers, Inc.

Chapter 70

ELECTRICAL TRANSPORT IN HYDROGENATED NANOCRYSTALLINE SILICON THIN FILMS

Sonia Beatriz Concari[*,1] *and Román Horacio Buitrago*[*,1,2]

[1]Departamento de Física - Facultad de Ingeniería Química (UNL) Stgo,
Santa Fe, Argentina
[2]Instituto de Desarrollo Tecnológico para la Industria Química
(CONICET - UNL)) Santa Fe, Argentina

RESEARCH SUMMARY

Different models for the electric charge flow in doped as well as in undoped hydrogenated nanocrystalline silicon (nc-Si:H) thin films have been proposed. However, there is no agreement about how the electrical transport occurs in these heterogeneous systems.

The electrical properties of nc-Si:H deposited using Very-High-Frequency Plasma-Enhanced Chemical Vapour Deposition (VH-PECVD) depend on the various deposition conditions, such as concentration of the dopant gases, ratio of hydrogen dilution, deposition temperature and pressure, radio frequency power, etc. The nucleation and the growth characteristics of the films are modified by these deposition parameters, changing the structural properties and therefore the electrical ones.

The effects of temperature (270–450 K) and applied electric field (0.1–2 x 10^4 V/cm) on the transport properties of intrinsic nc-Si:H thin films as well as p-type doped with Boron prepared by VH-PECVD are analysed. Variable Range Hopping (VRH) between defects near the Fermi level was established as a predominant electronic transport mechanism for intermediate applied fields.

At very low applied electric fields, dark conductivity becomes field-dependent. The non-ohmic behaviour of the conductivity observed is analysed in terms of the hopping transport equations.

---

[*] E-mail: sconcari@fiq.unl.edu.ar.
[*] E-mail: rbuitre@intec.unl.edu.ar.

Even when electronic transport is still not well understood, variable range hopping could highlight some mechanisms of current flow in non homogeneous semiconductor thin films. Other researchers have begun using the same model to fit experimental data of conductivity on many other mixed-phase thin film materials, even when no theory has been formulated to explain electrical transport in nanocrystalline thin films.

In: Materials Science Researcher Biographical Sketches ...   ISBN: 978-1-61942-153-0
Editors: Satomi Matsumoto and Ueda Iwate

Chapter 71

DEVELOPMENT IN MATERIALS PROCESSING OF MGB₂ - MICROSTRUCTURE, CHEMICAL DOPING AND CRITICAL CURRENT PROPERTIES

Akiyasu Yamamoto[*], *Jun-ichi Shimoyama*
and Kohji Kishio

Department of Applied Chemistry, University of Tokyo, Hongo,
Bunkyo-ku, Tokyo, Japan

RESEARCH SUMMARY

Since the discovery of superconductivity in magnesium diboride (MgB_2), large efforts have been made for improving its critical current density, which is one of the most important parameters for practical application. Among various methods, control of microstructure and chemical doping to MgB_2 are shown to be most effective for improving flux pinning strength and/or enhancing upper critical field. In this review, we report effects of low-temperature processing and carbon substitution on the microstructures and critical current properties of MgB_2 bulk samples. We have found that the mechanisms of the enhancement of critical current density by low-temperature processing and carbon substitution are universally explained by the concept of degrading of crystallinity. Based on the experimentally obtained results, we will discuss routes to improvement of critical current properties in the development of high performance MgB_2 materials.

[*] E-mail address: yamamoto@asc.magnet.fsu.edu. Present address: Applied Superconductivity Center, National High Magnetic Field Laboratory, Tallahassee, FL 32310, USA).

In: Materials Science Researcher Biographical Sketches …   ISBN: 978-1-61942-153-0

Editors: Satomi Matsumoto and Ueda Iwate   © 2013 Nova Science Publishers, Inc.

Chapter 72

INFLUENCE OF THERMOMECHANICAL TREATMENT ON MICROSTRUCTURE AND MECHANICAL PROPERTIES OF WEATHER RESISTANT STEEL

S. N. Prasad[*],[1] and D. S. Sarma[2]*

[1]Research and Development Centre for Iron and Steel,
Steel Authority of India Ltd., Doranda, Ranchi, India
[2]Professor (Retired), Metallurgical Engineering Department,
Institute of technology, Banaras Hindu University, Varanasi, India

RESEARCH SUMMARY

The influence of thermomechanical treatment (TMT) on the microstructure and mechanical properties of weather resistant steel (0.1 % C, 0.11 % P, 0.88 % Mn, 0.34 % Ni, 0.48 % Cr and 0.47 % Cu) has been studied. It has been found that the yield strength (YS) of the steel considerably increases when rolled to 50 % at 800 or 740^0C as compared to rolling at 900^0C, showing that even in the absence of microalloying it is amenable to thermomechanical treatment after an initial soaking at 1000^0C. The ultimate tensile strength (UTS), hardness and tensile ductility are, however, not significantly affected by the rolling temperature (900-740^0C) or deformation (25-50%). As in the thermomechanical treatment of microalloyed steel, the ferrite grain size decreases with decreasing rolling temperature and increasing deformation in this Cu-P-Cr-Ni-Mn weather resistant steel. The ferrite has a polygonal morphology, after rolling at 900^0C. However, multiple alloying additions, particularly higher Mn content in weather resistant steel, result in a mixed microstructure of polygonal ferrite, pearlite and non-polygonal ferrite with higher dislocation density, which is the characteristic of acicular ferrite, after rolling at 800^0C. In addition to polygonal ferrite and pearlite, subgrains also form after rolling at 740^0C. On the other hand, higher Mn (1.5%) and Nb

---

[*] E-mail address: snprasad1002@rediffmail.com; Telephone: +916512411070 Extension 2294; + 91 9431701971 (M); Fax: +916512411081. (Corresponding author)

(0.02%) microalloyed hot rolled, in multi passes, weather resistant steel shows a mixed microstructure consisting of ferrite, pearlite and bainite. This steel has got substantially higher UTS (853 MPa). The synergistic effect of Nb and Mn with other alloying elements produces higher bainitic hardenability resulting in formation of higher amount of bainite which increases the UTS of the steel remarkably.

In: Materials Science Researcher Biographical Sketches ...   ISBN: 978-1-61942-153-0
Editors: Satomi Matsumoto and Ueda Iwate   © 2013 Nova Science Publishers, Inc.

Chapter 73

TOMONAGA-LUTTINGER LIQUID BEHAVIOR IN CARBON NANOTUBES; THEORY AND SOLID STATE SPECTROSCOPY

Bal´azs D´ora[1,] and Ferenc Simon[2,†]*

[1]Max-Planck-Institut f¨ur Physik Komplexer Systeme, Dresden, Germany
[2]Budapest University of Technology and Economics, Institute of Physics
and Condensed Matter Research Group of the Hungarian Academy of Sciences,
Budapest, Hungary

RESEARCH SUMMARY

Single-wall carbon nanotubes (SWCNTs) are archetypes of one-dimensional objects with quasi one-dimensional electronic structure. As such, it is expected that they display unique and exotic correlated ground states. Here, we review recent experimental and theoretical advances in the description of their ground state, focusing on the so-called Tomonaga-Luttinger liquid (TLL) description. The TLL phase occurs in one-dimensional system with strong electron-electron interaction. Using bosonization, interacting fermions are represented by a non-interacting bosonic Hamiltonians with sound-like excitations. The correlation functions and the corresponding physical measurables follow power law behaviors which can be tested experimentally. It is now generally accepted that the SWCNT material is a unique example where the physics of the TLL state can be tested with a variety of methods. These include transport, photoemission spectroscopy, and magnetic resonance spectroscopy. We discuss how the TLL theory can be applied to account for the most recent magnetic resonance experiments, which solidifies the present understanding of both the TLL theory and the nature of the SWCNT ground state.

---

[*] E-mail address: dora@pks.mpg.de.
[†] E-mail address: ferenc.simon@univie.ac.at.

In: Materials Science Researcher Biographical Sketches ... ISBN: 978-1-61942-153-0

Editors: Satomi Matsumoto and Ueda Iwate © 2013 Nova Science Publishers, Inc.

Chapter 74

QUANTUM-VACUUM EFFECTS AND QUANTUM COHERENCE IN ARTIFICIAL ELECTROMAGNETICMATERIALS

Jian Qi Shen[*]

[1]Centre for Optical and Electromagnetic Research,
State Key Laboratory of Modern Optical Instrumentations,
Zijingang Campus, Zhejiang University,
Hangzhou, The People's Republic of China
[2]Joint Research Centre of Photonics of the Royal Institute
of Technology (Sweden) and Zhejiang University, Zijingang Campus,
Zhejiang University, Hangzhou, The People's Republic of China

RESEARCH SUMMARY

Artificial electromagnetic materials can be utilized to manipulate light propagations, and have potential applications in designs of photonic and quantum optical devices. Multilevel quantum coherent media is one kind of such artificial electromagnetic materials. Some physically interesting effects due to the combination of quantum coherence and quantum vacuum, *i.e.*, the tunable quantum coherent effects, in which the quantum-vacuum fluctuation field is involved, are suggested. Two topics are addressed: i) the spontaneous emission inhibition due to quantum interference in a three-level system; ii) the quantum light-induced potentials for coherent manipulation of atomic matter waves. The light-induced quantum guiding potentials could be utilized to cool and trap atoms, and may be used for the development of new techniques of atom fibers and atom chips, where the coherent manipulation of atomic matter waves is needed. In addition, the physical foundation of quantum coherence is analyzed and its counterparts in other fields are suggested. It is well known that the mechanism of atomic CPT (coherent population trapping) and EIT (electromagnetically induced transparency) is the quantum destructive interference. However, there are some interesting analogues in field theory such as quark mixing mechanism that also

---

[*] E-mail address: jqshen@coer.zju.edu.cn, jqshencn@yahoo.com.cn.

exhibits such a phase coherence. We compare the quantum interferences of the atomic CPT with the quark mixing (and GIM mechanism) in the weak interaction. It is shown that the quantum destructive interference presented here is one of the common characteristics of many quantum coherent processes. The scheme presented here may have a potential significance in both pure and applied physics, *e.g.*, providing us with a new insight into the physical essence of quantum coherence in various physical processes, and applying the quantum-vacuum effects to the development of new photonic devices.

In: Materials Science Researcher Biographical Sketches ...   ISBN: 978-1-61942-153-0
Editors: Satomi Matsumoto and Ueda Iwate   © 2013 Nova Science Publishers, Inc.

Chapter 75

AZOBENZENE CONTAINING POLYMERS: FUNDAMENTALS AND TECHNICAL APPLICATIONS

Yanhua Luo and Qijin Zhang

CAS Key Laboratory of Soft Matter Chemistry, Department of Polymer Science
and Engineering, University of Science and Technology of China
Key Laboratory of Optoelectronic Science and Technology,
Anhui Province, Hefei, Anhui, China

RESEARCH SUMMARY

Azobenzene doped or covalently bonded polymers (azopolymers in short) have been attracted much attention for their potential technological applications. Many of these applications are possible due to efficient photoisomerization and photoinduced anisotropy of the azobenzene groups. Research works and related technique developments in this field are reviewed, focusing on functionalities and characteristics of azopolymers, which include photoinduced refractive index change, liquid crystallinity, photoinduced phase transition, photowettability, nonlinear optical(NLO) properties, photoinduced alignment, and photoinduced birefringence(PIB) and chirality. Furthermore, some chemical and physical influencing factors upon the photoinduced processes have also been reviewed. Chemical factors are mainly about structures including covalently linked with the main chain, the substitutes linking to azobenzene, extending the conjugation of azobenzene by adding one azobenzence, the spacer length and cross-linking. And physical factors include the azo concentration, confinement effect, the film thickness, temperature, and pump beam type and intensity. Understanding the fundamental properties of azopolymers enables us to make use of these structures in a variety of applications, such as display devices, optical switching, optical waveguides, holography, coupler, mask, reversible optical storage, photomotor, DFB laser, polarizers and so on.

In: Materials Science Researcher Biographical Sketches …   ISBN: 978-1-61942-153-0
Editors: Satomi Matsumoto and Ueda Iwate   © 2013 Nova Science Publishers, Inc.

Chapter 76

CALCIUM ORTHOPHOSPHATE CEMENTS AND CONCRETES

Sergey V. Dorozhkin[*]
Moscow, Russia

RESEARCH SUMMARY

In the early 1980s, researchers discovered self-setting calcium orthophosphate cements, which are a bioactive and biodegradable grafting material in the form of a powder and a liquid. Both phases after mixing form a viscous paste that after being implanted sets and hardens within the body as either a non-stoichiometric calcium deficient hydroxyapatite (CDHA) or brushite, sometimes blended with unreacted particles and other phases. As both CDHA and brushite are remarkably biocompartible and bioresorbable (therefore, *in vivo* they can be replaced with a newly forming bone), calcium orthophosphate cements represent a good correction technique of non-weight-bearing bone fractures or defects and appear to be very promising materials for bone grafting applications. Besides, these cements possess an excellent osteoconductivity, molding capabilities and easy manipulation. Nearly perfect adaptation to the tissue surfaces in bone defects and a gradual bioresorption followed by new bone formation are additional distinctive advantages of calcium orthophosphate cements. Furthermore, reinforced cement formulations are available, which in a certain sense might be described as calcium orthophosphate concretes. The concepts established by calcium orthophosphate cement pioneers in the early 1980-s were used as a platform to initiate a new generation of bone substitute materials for commercialization. Since then, advances have been made in the composition, performance and manufacturing; several beneficial formulations have already been introduced as a result. Many other compositions are in experimental stages. In this review, an insight into calcium orthophosphate cements and concretes, as excellent biomaterials suitable for both dental and bone grafting application, has been provided.

---

[*] Corresponding author: Email: sedorozhkin@yandex.ru.

In: Materials Science Researcher Biographical Sketches ...   ISBN: 978-1-61942-153-0

Editors: Satomi Matsumoto and Ueda Iwate   © 2013 Nova Science Publishers, Inc.

Chapter 77

SINTER-ALLOYING AND PROPERTIES OF MANGANESE STEELS: STATE OF THE ART

Andrej Šalak and Marcela Selecká

Institute for Materials Research of Slovak Academy of Sciences,
Košice, Slovak Republic

RESEARCH SUMMARY

Manganese is the cheapest alloy element with high hardenability effect commonly used in wrought steels. Nevertheless, manganese was as an alloy element studied in powder metallurgy since ~1950 mainly under laboratory conditions. The hard reducibility of Mn oxides due to high affinity of manganese for oxygen, especially of MnO, requiring the purity of the sintering atmospheres not attainable in practice, is regarded for a technical problem. In this chapter are given the thermodynamic data (oxygen partial pressure, dew points of the atmosphere) required for the equilibrium conditions for Mn – O system. Mechanical properties of manganese steels attained prove successful sintering. The used sintering conditions for these steels did not fulfill the thermodynamic requirements for the tested systems. Some representative maximal tensile strength values attained are summarized. High vapor pressure characterizes manganese, and its values in dependence on temperature are presented demonstrating in a spontaneous sublimation. Effect of manganese vapor on alloying of iron powder matrix in the compacts is explained. The reaction of gaseous manganese with the oxygen in the atmosphere characterized. The result of this is the "self-cleaning" effect of manganese for sintering atmosphere to equilibrium conditions for Mn – O system. This process, given by physical property of manganese, is only one possible to secure effective sintering of mixed and hybrid manganese containing steels without other special measures.

In: Materials Science Researcher Biographical Sketches ...   ISBN: 978-1-61942-153-0
Editors: Satomi Matsumoto and Ueda Iwate   © 2013 Nova Science Publishers, Inc.

Chapter 78

MICROSTRUCTURALLY SHORT CRACKS IN POLYCRYSTALLS DESCRIBED BY CRYSTAL PLASTICITY

Leon Cizelj[*] and Igor Simonovski[†]
University of Ljubljana, Ljubljana, Slovenia

RESEARCH SUMMARY

Microstructurally short cracks with lengths up to about ten grains are known to be strongly influenced by the microstructural features in the neighborhood of the crack tip. These include randomly shaped and oriented crystal grains and strongly orientation dependent deformation behavior of the grains. The goal of our work is to propose computational models aiming to quantify the effects of random grain orientations on the variability of crack tip opening and sliding displacements (CTOD, CTSD).

A Voronoi tessellation based computational model has been developed to simulate the random grain structure. The constitutive behavior of individual grains includes randomly oriented anisotropic elasticity and crystal plasticity (where Schmid resolved stress is taken into account). The equilibrium equations are solved with macroscopic boundary conditions at the scale of the component using commercially available finite element solver ABAQUS.

The stationary crack configurations studied include transgranular crack extending through about half of a crystal grain, a series of cracks of different sizes simulating the short crack approaching and crossing the first grain boundary and a series of cracks with different lengths extending from one to over a few grains. The FCC material with properties representing industry grade austenitic stainless steel is assumed with macroscopic uniaxial loading approaching macroscopic yield strength of the material. Sufficiently many

---

[*] Ph.D., Senior Research Associate, »Jožef Stefan« Institute, and Associate Professor, University of Ljubljana, Ljubljana, Slovenia; Tel.: + 386 1 5885 215, Fax.: +386 1 5885 337, E-mail: Leon.Cizelj@ijs.si, Mail: »Jožef Stefan« Institute, Jamova cesta 39, SI-1000 Ljubljana, Slovenia.
[†] Ph.D., Research Associate, »Jožef Stefan« Institute, Ljubljana, Slovenia, Tel.: + 386 1 5885 290, Fax.: +386 1 5885 337, E-mail: Igor.Simonovski@ijs.si, Mail: »Jožef Stefan« Institute, Jamova cesta 39, SI-1000 Ljubljana, Slovenia.

simulations with different random grain orientations have been performed to arrive at approximate cumulative probability distributions of the CTOD and CTSD. Possible limits of the CTOD/CTSD variability, as for example those derived from a large monocrystal with variable lattice orientations with respect to the crack and from the linear elastic fracture mechanics, are given and discussed. Discussion includes identification of at least two main sources of the CTOD/CTSD variability: grain structure and strain localizations extending over the entire computational domain. Also, the attempt is made to quantify the decreasing influence of the grain structure with increasing crack length.

The current computational model is limited to an essentially planar model (plane strain) with lattice rotations around the out of plane axis only. This basically allows for limiting most of the slip to two active (inplane) slip systems. The reason for this is the computational intensity of the simulations. A limited amount of simulations with spatial lattice 3D material orientations has also been performed to quantify the consequences of planar approximation.

An outlook towards modeling of as-measured spatial microstructures and intergranular cracks is given.

In: Materials Science Researcher Biographical Sketches ...   ISBN: 978-1-61942-153-0
Editors: Satomi Matsumoto and Ueda Iwate   © 2013 Nova Science Publishers, Inc.

Chapter 79

COMPOSITE LAMINATES PERFORMANCE ENHANCEMENT BY NANOPARTICLES DISPERSION: AN INVESTIGATION ON HYBRID NANOCOMPOSITES

Antonio F. Avila[*]

Universidade Federal de Minas Gerais, Department of Mechanical Engineering,
NanoComposites Research Group, Belo Horizonte, MG, Brazil

RESEARCH SUMMARY

High performance polymeric composites (HPPC) are a valuable alternative to conventional materials due to their high specific mechanical properties, i.e. stiffness-to-weight and strength-to-weight, tailor-ability, and damage tolerance. HPPCs can have their performance improved by the addition of nanoparticles. These particles allow the formation of nanostructures inside the polymeric matrix leading to a complete different overall composite behavior. These nanomodified HPPCs are studied considering thermal stability, natural frequencies, the nanostructure morphology, void formation and mechanical properties under quasi-static and dynamic loadings. In all cases, the addition of nanoparticles, i.e. nanoclays or nanographite, leads to significant improvement. Each analysis technique is detailed and their pros and cons are discussed.

---

[*] Corresponding author: E-mail: aavila@netuno.lcc.ufmg.br.

In: Materials Science Researcher Biographical Sketches …   ISBN: 978-1-61942-153-0
Editors: Satomi Matsumoto and Ueda Iwate   © 2013Nova Science Publishers, Inc.

Chapter 80

RECENT DEVELOPMENT OF FULLERENOL RESEARCH

T. H. Goswami and *Rachana Singh*

Electronics and Smart Materials Division, Defence Materials & Stores Research
& Development Establishment, India

RESEARCH SUMMARY

Ever since the discovery and large scale production of *fullerene (C$_{60}$)*, an intensive research is on to explore and utilize the exotic properties of this aesthetic material. The early problems concerning the material tractability associated with the pristine fullerene were thoroughly addressed and efforts have been focused on the molecular engineering of structures in order to produce materials possessing enhanced electrical and optical properties. Derivatization of fullerene (atom / group /organic moiety) not only amicably solves the tractability problem but also enhances its scope to exploit these materials for wide variety of novel applications. Among the functionalized derivatives, *fullerenol* [C$_{60}$(OH)$_x$], the polyhydroxy fullerene, has been extensively studied owing to its high solubility in large variety of solvents (depending on the number of hydroxyl groups the solubility varies from organic to aqueous), good stability (in ambient condition) and extremely high reactivity. Pure (unreacted) fullerenols have been explored for the development of buffer layers for fullerene / conducting polymer solar cells, as an actuator to study piezoelectric effect on doped polyurethane elastomers and free-radical scavenger against reactive oxygen species (ROS) and OH⁻ radicals as well as nitric oxides. Fullerenols have also been studied as proton conductors in fuel-cells and the size controllable supramolecular self-assembly of nanospheres and nanocomposites.

The strong nucleophilic (acidic) character also makes fullerenol an excellent precursor for the development of newer materials combining the unique properties of fullerene with the excellent properties of the addended materials. The fulleroxide [fol]$^{n-}$ nucleophile generated

---

* Corresponding author: Fax: + 91- 512 – 2450404 / 2404774, E-mail: thgoswami@yahoo.co.uk; thakohari_ goswami@rediffmail.com.

by release of proton undergoes several interesting reaction pathways; 1) selective nucleophilic addition reactions to the carbonyl group, 2) Michael addition reaction with α, β-unsaturated esters, 3) nucleophilic displacement as well as transesterification reaction with silicon derivatives and 4) nucleophilic addition reaction to isocyanates.

However, the most important aspect in developing such material is to use an isomerically pure fullerenol. Although various methods have been developed for their synthesis, these methods usually give a high level of hydroxylation and inseparable complicated mixtures of isomers. The preparation of isomerically pure fullerenol remains a challenge ever since its synthesis which has been nicely addressed in some recent reports. The stability of these fullerenols are also well studied.

The chapter will bring out all these excellent developments in fullerenol research since the last ten years. Earlier developments will be incorporated as a reference and will be discussed only when a comparison is required. To conclude, the chapter will provide an essence to the all-round development of fullerenol research to its readers and researchers.

In: Materials Science Researcher Biographical Sketches …   ISBN: 978-1-61942-153-0
Editors: Satomi Matsumoto and Ueda Iwate   © 2013 Nova Science Publishers, Inc.

Chapter 81

IMPACT OF INORGANIC PARTICLES ON THE POLYMER COMPOSITE AND ITS APPLICATION TO SPECIAL EFFECT

*Yong-Chan Chung[1] and Byoung Chul Chun[2,]**

[1]Department of Chemistry, The University of Suwon, Suwon, Korea
[2]Department of Polymer Engineering, The University of Suwon, Suwon, Korea

RESEARCH SUMMARY

Inorganic particles such as montmorillonite (MMT), celite, or shell powder were melt-mixed with polyurethane (PU) or polyethylene (PE), and the resultant polymer composites were analyzed and applied to special effects. First, nanocomposite from polyurethane and montmorillonite was prepared by a twin screw extruder, together with a compatibilizer to enhance dispersion of MMT (Cloisite 25A or Cloisite 30B). Maleic anhydride grafted polypropylene (MAPP) was used as the compatibilizer. Nanoparticle dispersion was the best at 1 wt% of MMT, and improved with the compatibilizer content for both composites. Properties of the composites such as complex viscosity and storage modulus were higher than those of pure PU matrix, and increased with MMT but decreased with the compatibilizer content. Second, a PU was cross-linked by celite, a porous inorganic material with enormous surface area and hydroxyl groups on the surface, to see if the shape memory effect and the mechanical properties were improved. The shape memory effect and mechanical properties were dependent on the celite content. The inclusion of celite as a cross-linker increased both shape memory effect and mechanical properties. The reasons underlining the improvements by adopting celite as a cross-linker are discussed. Third, a celite surface-modified with cationic surfactant was used as an additive in polyethylene (PE) for high odor storing capacity and long odor lasting period. The PE with cetyltrimethylammonium bromide (CTAB)-modified celite showed the best odor storing and lasting properties. Comparisons among the different types were made, together with brief discussion about the reason for differences in odor lasting period. Finally, A series of PE and oyster-shell powder was prepared to test their

* Corresponding author: Email: bcchun@suwon.ac.kr.

fire-retardant properties. Oyster-shell powder was mainly composed of calcium carbonate and decomposed to calcium oxide and carbon dioxide at temperature higher than ca. 800 °C, thus preventing fire from access of oxygen by the produced carbon dioxide. This fire-retardation mechanism is environmentally friendly since other available method such as the inclusion of halogen-containing compounds normally generates toxic chemicals like dioxine during incineration. Flame retardation and the mechanical properties of these composite resins were analyzed.

In: Materials Science Researcher Biographical Sketches …   ISBN: 978-1-61942-153-0

Editors: Satomi Matsumoto and Ueda Iwate   © 2013 Nova Science Publishers, Inc.

Chapter 82

DIFFERENT ASPECTS OF APPLICATION OF LIQUID CRYSTALS IN CHOLESTERIC AND PRETRANSITIONAL PHASES

Guram Chilaya[*]

Institute of Cybernetics, Tbilisi, Georgia

RESEARCH SUMMARY

Cholesteric liquid crystals (CLCs) and pretransitional twist grain boundary (TGB) and blue phases (BPs), owing the self-organized periodical structure, sensitive to external fields, have provide several opportunities for creation new photonic and optoelectronic devices. In this paper results in electrooptics and photooptics of CLCs and pretransitional phases will be reviewed. The review consists 5 paragraphs. 1. Electrooptics of cholesterics. 2. Photooptics of cholesterics. 3. Light induced permanent gratings and displays in a luminescent dye doped cholesterics 4. Electrooptics and photooptics of blue phases. 5. Mirrorless lasing in an intermediate between cholesteric and smectic A phases.

[*] Corresponding author: Email: chilaya@yahoo.com.

In: Materials Science Researcher Biographical Sketches ...   ISBN: 978-1-61942-153-0
Editors: Satomi Matsumoto and Ueda Iwate   © 2013 Nova Science Publishers, Inc.

Chapter 83

BIODEGRADABLE HYDROGELS AS DRUG DELIVERY SYSTEMS FOR TISSUE ENGINEERING APPLICATIONS

G. Kacey Marra[1-4] and J. Alicia DeFail[2]
[1]Division of Plastic and Reconstructive Surgery, University of Pittsburgh, Pittsburgh, PA, US
[2]Department of Bioengineering, University of Pittsburgh, Pittsburgh, PA, US
[3]Department of Surgery, University of Pittsburgh, Pittsburgh, PA, US
[4]McGowan Institute for Regenerative Medicine, Pittsburgh, PA, US

RESEARCH SUMMARY

Tissue engineering is a potential therapeutic strategy which combines scaffolds, cells, and/or growth factors that provide a suitable environment to direct the growth of new, healthy tissue. Scaffolds that are biodegradable, biocompatible, mechanically support tissue growth, and can be shaped to fill an irregularly shaped defect are ideal. Polymeric poly(lactic-*co*-glycolic acid) (PLGA) biomaterials are among the most widely studied tissue-engineered scaffolds. However, polymeric hydrogels, such as poly(ethylene glycol) (PEG) are also being examined as drug delivery scaffolds. Delivery of drugs or growth factors from these scaffolds is desirable to enhance tissue regeneration. The delivery of drugs or growth factors can be controlled by various parameters such as drug loading, polymer composition, and processing techniques. Drugs can also be encapsulated in microspheres or nanospheres for controlled delivery. Other methods of delivery include adsorption of drugs or growth factors to the surface prior to implantation or incorporation during the scaffold fabrication process. The incorporation of microspheres within PLGA scaffolds, fibrin scaffolds, gelatin scaffolds, and poly(ethylene glycol)-based hydrogels is also an option. This chapter describes several of these approaches that results in a controlled, localized release of drugs from the biomaterials. Clinical applications that will be discussed include bone regeneration, breast cancer adjuvant therapies, and nerve regeneration.

In: Materials Science Researcher Biographical Sketches ...   ISBN: 978-1-61942-153-0
Editors: Satomi Matsumoto and Ueda Iwate   © 2013 Nova Science Publishers, Inc.

Chapter 84

FREE VIBRATION ANALYSIS OF GENERALLY LAMINATED COMPOSITE PLATES BY THE INVERSE MULTIQUADRIC RADIAL BASIS FUNCTIONS AND FIRST-ORDER SHEAR DEFORMATION THEORY

Song Xiang Ke-ming Wang Ming-sui Yang and Guang-chao Li
College of Aeroengine & Energy Engineering, Shenyang Institute of Aeronautical Engineering, Shenyang, People's Republic of China

RESEARCH SUMMARY

In this paper we used a meshless collocation method based on the inverse multiquadric radial basis functions and first-order shear deformation theory to analyze free vibration of generally laminated composite plates. The governing differential equations and boundary conditions are dicretized into sets of linear equations in terms of displacement components. These equations yield a standard eigenvalue problem, which can be solved by a standard eigenvalue solver. Natural frequencies computed by the present method are found to agree well with those from some available published results, which demonstrate the high numerical accuracy and good convergence of the inverse multiquadric radial basis function for free vibration analysis of generally laminated composite plates.

In: Materials Science Researcher Biographical Sketches …   ISBN: 978-1-61942-153-0
Editors: Satomi Matsumoto and Ueda Iwate   © 2013Nova Science Publishers, Inc.

Chapter 85

GRAPH-SKEIN MODULES OF THREE-MANIFOLDS

Nafaa Chbili[*]
Department of Mathematical Sciences
United Arab Emirates University Al Ain, U.A.E.

RESEARCH SUMMARY

Our main purpose is to introduce the theory of graph-skein modules of three-manifolds. This theory associates to each oriented three-manifold M an algebraic object (a module or an algebra) which is defined by considering the set of all ribbon graphs embedded in M modulo local linear skein relations. This idea is inspired by Przytycki's theory of skein modules which is also known as algebraic topology based on knots. Historically, this theory appeared as a generalization of the quantum invariants of links in the three-sphere to links in an arbitrary three-manifold. In this paper, we review the construction of the Kauffman bracket skein module and investigate its relationship with our graph-skein modules. We compute the graph-skein algebra in few cases. As an application we introduce new criteria for symmetries of spatial graphs which improve some results obtained earlier. The proof of these criteria is based on some easy calculation in the graph-skein module of the solid torus.

[*] Corresponding address: Email: nafaachbili@uaeu.ac.ae.

In: Materials Science Researcher Biographical Sketches …   ISBN: 978-1-61942-153-0
Editors: Satomi Matsumoto and Ueda Iwate   © 2013 Nova Science Publishers, Inc.

Chapter 86

MODELING THE PLASTICITY OF NANOPOROUS NI/YSZ HIGH TEMPERATURE FUEL CELL ANODE UNDER UNIAXIAL LOADING

Yong X. Gan[*]

Department of Mechanical, Industrial and
Manufacturing Engineering, College of Engineering,
The University of Toledo, Toledo, OH, US

RESEARCH SUMMARY

Thin electrolytes yttria-stabilized zirconia (YSZ) and anode-supported (nanoporous Ni-YSZ) cells operating in the temperature range of 650-850°C are considered as promising solid oxide fuel cell systems. Understanding the thermalmechanical deformation behavior of the Ni/YSZ interface is critical for the design and durability assessment of the YSZ high temperature fuel cells. One of the problems still remains to be solved is the microstructure instability of the nanoporous Ni at the elevated temperatures. In this work, modeling the thermal-mechanical deformation in the nanoporous Ni/YSZ interface region was performed. Nanoporous Ni thin film bounded to YSZ was considered to establish a simplified 2-D model. On the Ni/YSZ interface, the nanopores are modeled as spherical or cylindrical pores. Crystal lattice rotation due to dislocation motion was simulated and the numerical solutions to the in-plane lattice rotation for the nanoporous Ni was used to predict the microstructure evolution in the interface area of the Ni/YSZ anode. The loading level effect was examined and the yield surface was constructed and compared with the analytical solutions.

[*] Corresponding author: E-mail: yong.gan@utoledo.edu, Tel: +1-419-530-6007; Fax: +1-419-530-8206.

In: Materials Science Researcher Biographical Sketches …   ISBN: 978-1-61942-153-0
Editors: Satomi Matsumoto and Ueda Iwate   © 2013 Nova Science Publishers, Inc.

Chapter 87

CONTINUUM DISLOCATION THEORY AND RELATED SIZE EFFECTS IN CRYSTAL PLASTICITY

Dennis M. Kochmann and Khanh C. Le[*]
Lehrstuhl f¨ur Allgemeine Mechanik, Ruhr-Universit¨at Bochum,
Bochum, Germany

RESEARCH SUMMARY

This Chapter discusses the continuum dislocation theory and its applications in crystal plasticity. We aim at studying the dislocation nucleation and accumulation, the resulting work hardening and the influence of the resistance to dislocation motion. Among boundary-value problems we consider plane constrained shear, plane strain uniaxial extension and their combination for single and bi-crystals, which admit analytical solutions. The interesting features of these solutions are the energetic and dissipative thresholds for dislocation nucleation, the Bauschinger translational work hardening, and the size effects.

[*] Corresponding author: E-mail chau.le@rub.de telephone +49-234-3226033, telefax +49-234-3206033.

In: Materials Science Researcher Biographical Sketches ...   ISBN: 978-1-61942-153-0
Editors: Satomi Matsumoto and Ueda Iwate   © 2013 Nova Science Publishers, Inc.

Chapter 88

RICE HUSK AS AS SUPPLEMENTARY CEMENTING MATERIAL

Gemma Rodríguez de Sensale[*]

Instituto de la Construcción-Instituto de Ensayo de
Materiales Universidad de la República, Montevideo, Uruguay

RESEARCH SUMMARY

This paper presents a study on the effects of rice-husk ash (RHA) as supplementary cementing material. The behavior of cementititious products varies with the source of the RHA. Two different RHAs, both amorphous and partially cristalline, and different replacement percentages of cement by RHA, are reported. The optimization of the RHA partially cristalline for their use as supplementary cementing material is presented. The properties investigated included setting times, autogenous deformation, compressive strength, splitting tensile strength, modulus of rupture, modulus of elasticity, air permeability, chloride penetration ions, alkali-silica expansion, acid and sulfate resistance. The results were compared with those of the reference without RHA. From the tested properties, it is concluded that the two types of ash used provide a possitive effect and reveal the holistic behavior of the RHA as supplementary cementing material.

---

[*] E-mail address: gemma@farq.edu.uy, gemma@fing.edu.uy. (Corresponding author)

In: Materials Science Researcher Biographical Sketches …   ISBN: 978-1-61942-153-0
Editors: Satomi Matsumoto and Ueda Iwate   © 2013 Nova Science Publishers, Inc.

Chapter 89

Magnetic Properties of the Diluted Magnetic Semiconductor Hg1-xMnxTe and Cd1-xMnxTe Monocrystals

Wang Zewen[1,2,*], Jie Wanqi[2] and Luan Lijun[2]

[1]Department of Electronic Engineering, Tsinghua University, Beijing, China
[2]School of Materials Science and Engineering, Northwestern Polytechnical University, Xi'an, China

Research Summary

Diluted magnetic semiconductor (DMS) generically encompasses a wide range of semiconductor alloys formed by the substitutional introduction of magnetic ions into a compound semiconductor. Taken in this most general sense, DMS materials include such diverse systems as $Zn_{1-x}Mn_xSe$, $Pb_{1-x}Eu_xTe$ and $(Cd_{1-x}Mn_x)_2As_3$. In $A_{1-x}^{II}Mn_xB^{VI}$ ternary alloy, Mn^{++} is randomly substituted for the cation of a II-VI semiconductor. It has gained much attention recently. The presence of the manganese ions Mn^{++} in $A_{1-x}^{II}MnxB^{VI}$ leads to an exchange interaction between the sp band electrons and the d electrons associated with Mn^{++} in the magnetic field, resulting in a series of dramatic new effects, such as the giant Faraday rotation, the magnetic-field-induced metal-insulator transition, the occurrence of large positive g factor, vanishing of Shubnikov-de Haas oscillations and giant negative magnetoresistance .

In the present paper, the magnetic susceptibility and magnetization of $Hg_{0.89}Mn_{0.11}Te$ under a series of constant temperature and magnetic field strength will be studied. The dependence of resistivity of $Hg_{0.89}Mn_{0.11}Te$ on the magnetic field up to 6.5 Tesla, and the temperature from 5 K to 200 K are also presented. Finally, the room-temperature Faraday rotation of $Cd_{1-x}Mn_xTe$ (x=0.1, 0.2) were measured.

---

[*] E-mail address: wzwen@tsinghua.edu.cn, Tel.: +86-10-62782734; Fax: +86-10-62784900. (Corresponding author).

In: Materials Science Researcher Biographical Sketches …   ISBN: 978-1-61942-153-0
Editors: Satomi Matsumoto and Ueda Iwate   © 2013 Nova Science Publishers, Inc.

Chapter 90

THE CHLORIDE MIGRATION COEFFICIENT OF PERCOLATED INTERFACIAL ZONE IN CEMENTITIOUS MATERIALS

Chung-Chia Yang[1], Shih-Wei Cho[2] and Yu-Ming Tsai[1]

[1]Institute of Materials Engineering, National Taiwan Ocean University,
Keelung, Taiwan, R.O.C.
[2]Department of Architecture, China University of Science and Technology,
Taipei, Taiwan, R.O.C.

RESEARCH SUMMARY

In this chapter the electrochemical technique is applied to accelerate chloride ion migration in cement-based material to estimate its migration coefficient. The chloride migration coefficient of cement-based material was obtained by using the accelerated chloride migration test (ACMT) and measured as a function of volume fraction of aggregate and the total lateral surface area of aggregate. In order to investigate the chloride migration coefficient of percolated ITZ on the chloride migration coefficient of specimen, specimens with cylindrical aggregates of the same height as the specimen were cast and tested. The volume fraction of aggregate is constant, and the varied lateral surface area of the aggregate cylinder was obtained by using different diameters and number of aggregate. A model obtained for the migration coefficient of cement-based material, and the regression analysis is used to determine the approximate chloride migration coefficient of the percolated ITZ. Based on the experimental and regression analytical results, the approximate percolated ITZ migration coefficient is approximate 40 to 35 times of the altered migration coefficient of matrix mortar for the w/c ratio of 0.35 to 0.55.

In: Materials Science Researcher Biographical Sketches …   ISBN: 978-1-61942-153-0
Editors: Satomi Matsumoto and Ueda Iwate   © 20133Nova Science Publishers, Inc.

Chapter 91

MODELLING OF MICROCRACKED BODIES USING THE CONCEPT OF CRACK OPENING MODE

A. Thionnet*
Centre des Matriaux, Mines Paristech, CNRS UMR, Evry cedex, France
Universit de Bourgogne, Dijon, France

RESEARCH SUMMARY

Damage present in a material in the form of plane cracks induces the decrease of some of its mechanical properties. For example, in the case of a tensile loading, and according to the plane in which the cracks are located, a decrease of the axial modulus can be observed.

The same observation can be made for the shear modulus in the case of a shear loading. If the sign of the loading changes, the axial modulus is restored. It is not the case for the shear modulus. This effect is usually called the unilateral effect of damage or damage activation/deactivation.

The modelling that can be made of the damageable elastic behavior of a microcracked body needs to be written in a way that takes into account:

($c1$): any discontinuity in the stress/strain relation;
($c2$): anisotropy induced by damage;
($c3$): decreases of the appropriate modulus;
($c4$): damage activation/deactivation.

In: Materials Science Researcher Biographical Sketches …   ISBN: 978-1-61942-153-0
Editors: Satomi Matsumoto and Ueda Iwate   © 2013Nova Science Publishers, Inc.

Chapter 92

DAMAGE-INDUCED ANISOTROPY AND THE INDETERMINATION OF DAMAGE TENSOR AT REST

Antonio Rinaldi[*,1,2,3]

[1]Department of Safety Technologies (DTS), ISPESL, Roma, Italy
[2]NAST Center & Department of Chemical Science and Technology, University of Rome Tor Vergata, Roma, Italy
[3]ASSOINGE R&D, AS, Rijswijk, The Netherlands

RESEARCH SUMMARY

The definition of the damage parameter for a multiaxial loading is a topic of exceptional complexity. This letter offers a perspective about the subject and puts in evidence five key concepts that may presumably contribute to shape future thinking and developments in microcracks research. Limiting the scope only to quasi-brittle failures for argument sake, a pure damage process consists of multisite microcracks formation and is perceived as a depletion of elastic properties. A microcrack is here regarded as the damage unit, representing the minimum packet of detectable or perceivable damage.

[*] E-mail address: antonio.rinaldi@ispesl.it or antonio.rinaldi@uniroma2.it or antonio.rinaldi@assoinge.org. (Corresponding author)

In: Materials Science Researcher Biographical Sketches ...   ISBN: 978-1-61942-153-0
Editors: Satomi Matsumoto and Ueda Iwate   © 2013 Nova Science Publishers, Inc.

Chapter 93

CHARACTERIZATION OF ASPHALTENES AND CRUDE OILS BY NEAR-UV/VISIBLE ABSORPTION SPECTROSCOPY

Igor N. Evdokimov[*]

Department of Physics, Gubkin Russian State University
of Oil and Gas, Moscow, Russia

RESEARCH SUMMARY

New experimental data as well as analysis of published databases show that the potential of UV-Visible absorption (UVVA) spectroscopy for characterization of asphaltenes may be strongly underestimated. Even the simplest single-parameter models for monotonous UVVA spectra of asphaltenes allow distinguishing various types of crude oils. The main practical problem is that generally crude oils and solutions of asphaltenes are opaque and have to be strongly diluted for UVVA analysis. Our experiments show that dilution may notably affect the measured UVVA spectra apparently due to de-aggregation of asphaltenes in a solution. In fact, previously reported UVVA spectra of asphaltenes/crude oils may have been strongly distorted by artifacts, affecting not only quantitative parameters (spectra's slopes), but also qualitative features (a presence of strong "resonance" absorption peaks). In particular, the popular "Urbach tail" model implies that the slopes of UVVA spectra reflect population (molecular weight) distributions of asphaltenes. This interpretation is obviously incompatible with the newly observed concentration effects in toluene solutions. On the other hand, our experimental data as well as critical analysis of other publications on optical spectroscopy of asphaltenes, show that the mythical "resonance absorption" is merely a solvent-related artifact and should be disregarded as basically erroneous.

Further development of UVVA characterization techniques requires better understanding of the nature/composition of asphaltenes. A useful approach may be consideration of "molecular diversity" models, being developed for other systems with continuous UVVA spectra, in particular for humic acids and melanins.

[*] Corresponding author: E-mail address: physexp@gubkin.ru.

In: Materials Science Researcher Biographical Sketches ...   ISBN: 978-1-61942-153-0
Editors: Satomi Matsumoto and Ueda Iwate   © 2013 Nova Science Publishers, Inc.

Chapter 94

EFFECT OF ASPHALTENE CONSTITUENTS ON REFINERY PROCESSES AND PRODUCTS

Irena Gawel[1] and James Speight[2]

[1]Wroclaw University of Technology, Department of Chemistry and Technology
of Fuels, Wroclaw, Poland
[2]CD & W Inc., Laramie, Wyoming, US

RESEARCH SUMMARY

The increasing production of heavy crude oil with a higher content of asphaltene constituents make the production and processing of heavy oil more difficult and costly. The asphaltene fraction consists of the highest molecular weight and the most polar fraction in crude oil and these constituents play a major role in the formation of deposits. Part of the reason for deposit formation is the means of dispersion of the asphaltene constituents within the oil, which is a delicately balanced system. It takes very little internal or external influence to upset this balance. Once the balance is upset, asphaltene constituents can cause a variety of problems during production, transportation, refining, and utilization of petroleum.

This review presents an overview of asphaltene in petroleum and the cause of sediment deposition during production and refining.

In: Materials Science Researcher Biographical Sketches ...   ISBN: 978-1-61942-153-0
Editors: Satomi Matsumoto and Ueda Iwate   © 2013 Nova Science Publishers, Inc.

Chapter 95

ASPHALT SURFACES AS ECOLOGICAL TRAPS FOR WATER-SEEKING POLAROTACTIC INSECTS: HOW CAN THE POLARIZED LIGHT POLLUTION OF ASPHALT SURFACES BE REDUCED?

Péter Malik[1], Ramón Hegedüs[2], György Kriska[3], Susanne Åkesson[4], Bruce Robertson[5] and Gábor Horváth[1]*

[1]Biooptics Laboratory, Department of Biological Physics, Physical Institute, Eötvös University, Budapest, Hungary
[2]Computer Vision and Robotics Group, University of Girona, Campus de Montilivi, Girona, Spain
[3]Group for Methodology in Biology Teaching, Biological Institute, Eötvös University, Budapest, Hungary
[4]Department of Animal Ecology, Lund University, Ecology Building, Lund, Sweden
[5]W. K. Kellogg Biological Station, Michigan State University, MI, US

RESEARCH SUMMARY

The surface of dry or wet asphalt roads reflects partially linearly polarized light, the degree of linear polarization p of which depends on the darkness and roughness of asphalt: the darker and/or the smoother the asphalt, the higher the p of light reflected from it. If the asphalt is sunlit and the direction of view is parallel to the solar-antisolar meridian, then the direction of polarization of asphalt-reflected light is horizontal. In this case the asphalt surface can attract water-seeking aquatic insects, because they detect water by means of the horizontal polarization of light reflected from the water surface. This phenomenon is called positive polarotaxis. Polarotactic insects mistaking asphalt surfaces for water bodies lay their eggs upon dry asphalt after copulation, where the eggs perish due to dehydration. The polarization signal of the asphalt surface can be so strong that insects can actively prefer

* Corresponding author: e-mail address: gh@arago.elte.hu.

asphalt over water as an oviposition site. This phenomenon is well studied for mass-swarming mayflies, but other polarotactic insects, such as dragonflies, caddisflies, stoneflies, water beetles and aquatic bugs can also be deceived by and attracted to asphalt roads near natural water bodies. We refer to the negative survival and reproductive consequences of artificial sources of polarized light on polarotactic organisms as polarized light pollution. Highly and horizontally polarizing asphalt roads are sources of polarized light pollution that can create ecological traps for polarotactic insects when they become more attractive than natural habitats. Trapped populations are predicted to have a high probability of extinction, and so paved surfaces may threaten populations of endangered aquatic insect species. An ecological trap for water insects can further trigger a secondary ecological trap for other vertebrate species that prey upon the water insects attracted to the asphalt: these insects and the carcasses of vehicle-killed polarotactic insects can attract different insectivorous vertebrates, especially birds, which can also be run down by the cars. In this work we study the polarizing characteristics of asphalt surfaces as functions of the surface features (roughness, darkness, painted with white striates or not), the illumination conditions (sunny or shady), and the direction of view relative to the solar meridian. On the basis of these data we suggest some possible strategies to mitigate the severity of polarized light pollution produced by asphalt. In areas with gravel roads, for example, change of the gravel to the more insect-attracting asphalt should, if possible, be avoided. We show how the degree of polarization p of asphalt-reflected light can be reduced under the threshold of polarization sensitivity of aquatic insects: the roughness, brightness and white-striateness of the asphalt surface should be increased in order to reduce p, and thus the attractiveness to polarotactic insects. We propose the use of these remedies on asphalt roads running near emergence sites of endangered aquatic insects, especially in the vicinity of wetlands, rivers and lakes. Conservation biologists may effect substantial benefits for aquatic insects and their ecosystems by working with asphalt road planners to reduce the attractiveness of asphalt surfaces to polarotactic species.

In: Materials Science Researcher Biographical Sketches …   ISBN: 978-1-61942-153-0
Editors: Satomi Matsumoto and Ueda Iwate   © 2013 Nova Science Publishers, Inc.

Chapter 96

EFFECT OF MAGNETIC FIELD ON THE PARAMAGNETIC, ANTIOXIDANT, AND VISCOUS PROPERTIES OF OILS AND RESIN-ASPHALTENE COMPONENTS

Yu. V. Loskutova

Institute of Petroleum Chemistry, Siberian Branch
of the Russian Academy of Sciences, Russia

RESEARCH SUMMARY

In the last few years, problems concerning mechanisms of structurization in dispersed oil systems under the influence of external factors and their relation with rheological (viscous and temperature) properties have been discussed extensively in the literature. An increased interest of the researchers is caused by the fact that only deep and profound knowledge of the nature of dispersions in oil systems allows a problem of forming resin-asphaltene-paraffin depositions (RAPD) to be solved and physical and chemical principles of the technology of control over the rheological oil properties under conditions of oil recovery, transportation, and storage to be developed.

In recent years, interest of the researchers in low-energy action on substances aimed at the alteration of their properties has been increased. It appeared that the material structure can be reorganized in the required direction without significant external energy consumption or with the use of internal reserves. Various electric, electromagnetic, magnetic, vibration, and acoustic fields are conventionally used to control the material structure. In this case, effects of increase or, on the contrary, decrease (in the process of decomposition) in ordering of supermolecular structures are attained fairly easily.

Low-energy technologies are being increasingly employed in petroleum industry. Their use allows a significant degree of dissociation of oil associates formed by resin-asphaltene components (RAC) and crystalline paraffin hydrocarbons to be achieved in a short time and then to be retained during the period of time necessary for realization of mass-exchange processes.

In the last few years, the method of magnetic treatment (MT) with the help of special devices – magnetic activators – is increasingly employed to improve the rheological properties of oil systems and to decrease resin-asphaltene-paraffin and salt deposition on the walls of industrial equipment. The magnetic activators are fixed in a well or pipeline in front of the intensive RAPD zone. They decrease the pipeline corrosion rate by factors of 2–10, increase the period of well operation without cleaning by factors of 3–10, and retain the MT effect for ≤72 h. However, industrial tests in a number of oil fields have revealed both positive effects and negative consequences of the use of the magnetic activators for control of oil depositions.

A wider application of economic and accessible magnetic field energy is limited by insufficient theoretical knowledge of the versatile action of magnetic field forces and the complexity of structural and energetic transformations proceeding on micro- and macrolevels in various substances. The lack of a standard and scientifically proved mechanism describing the behavior of dispersed oil systems (DOS) in magnetic fields often does not allow possible effects to be predicted and the magnetic activators with optimal parameters to be designed.

Several qualitative theories have been known that underlie the mechanism of magnetic field action on the DOS. Among them are *colloid* hypotheses according to which the magnetic field acts on colloid para-, dia-, and ferromagnetic particles; *ionic* hypotheses in which the main role is assigned to ions localized in water, and *water* hypotheses substantiating the magnetic field action on the water itself. The mechanism of magnetic field action on aqueous systems is reduced to the change of microimpurity bonds with molecules of the liquid environment. Water theories have become fairly popular with reference to the magnetic field action on the physical and chemical properties of oil and water-oil liquid environments. They are based on dissociation of iron-containing particle aggregates in the magnetic field. However, it is impossible to assign to the iron microimpurities, being one of the components of the mineral structure of mechanical impurities in oils, the unique and determining role in the processes proceeding in oils exposed to the magnetic field. According to the colloid theory, the mechanism of magnetic field influence on substances is based on different types of the behavior of diamagnetic and paramagnetic molecules in the external magnetic field. According to this theory, resins and asphalthenes presented in oils are substances of paraelectric, paramagnetic, and diamagnetic types. The presence of ferromagnets (Fe, V, Ni, etc.) in oil also supplements complicated spatial interactions of diamagnetic and paramagnetic oil components in the magnetic field.

In the ideal case, the mechanism of magnetic field influence on the oil systems must take into account the elemental oil composition, that is, the contents and chemical features of the structure of resins, asphaltenes, and paraffin hydrocarbons as well as the presence of liquid and gaseous phases and microimpurities. Therefore, only a comprehensive study of the behavior of oils having various compositions in the magnetic field will add significantly to our knowledge of the influence of physical fields on various structured systems, including the examined dispersed colloid oil systems.

The present work studies the special features of the structural-rheological behavior of oils and their resin-asphaltene fractions after treatment by a sigh-alternating magnetic field.

In: Materials Science Researcher Biographical Sketches …   ISBN: 978-1-61942-153-0
Editors: Satomi Matsumoto and Ueda Iwate   © 2013Nova Science Publishers, Inc.

Chapter 97

Occlusion Inside Asphaltene Aggregates: Insights into the Structural Characteristics of Asphaltenes and its Geochemical Significance

Zewen Liao[1], Patrice Creux[2], Chupeng Yang[1,3], Alain Graciaa[2] and Anna Chrostowska[2]

[1]State Key Laboratory of Organic Geochemistry, Guangzhou Institute of Geochemistry, Chinese Academy of Sciences, Guangzhou, P. R. China
[2]Laboratoire des Fluides Complexes, Pau Cedex, France
[3]Guangzhou Marine Geological Survey, Ministry of Land and Resources, Guangzhou, P. R. China

Research Summary

Asphaltene molecules are characterized by aromatic ring units attached to plenty of aliphatic chains and some heteroatoms, and they have the capacity to fold upon themselves into a complex three-dimensional globular configuration with internal structures. This kind of structural features enable asphaltenes to form substantial microporous units, and thus liable to adsorb and occlude the other fractions in the crude oil. The occluded compounds inside asphaltene aggregates can be released through mild degradation processes oxidized by H_2O_2/CH_3COOH system. The occlusion results indicate that asphaltene aggregates are the stable species even in toluene, and then they can stably exist in the oil reservoirs underground to survive the long geological timescale on a much more extensive scale with larger sizes. These occluded compounds are realized as the original oil from kerogen, which were generated from kerogen at a low matured level and then occluded inside asphaltenes and have survived the long geological timescale owing to the effective protection from asphaltene macromolecular structures. Some biogenic compounds have been detected from the occluded fraction inside asphaltenes, which were not detected directly from the maltenes. The geochemical significance of these occluded compounds deserves some more efforts to probe its application into the field of oil reservoir geochemistry, especially for the heavily altered oils such as biodegraded oils from which it is difficult to obtain useful geochemical information directly from the maltenes because in which the hydrocarbons have been heavily depleted.

In: Materials Science Researcher Biographical Sketches …   ISBN: 978-1-61942-153-0
Editors: Satomi Matsumoto and Ueda Iwate   © 2013 Nova Science Publishers, Inc.

Chapter 98

TOWARDS PEDIATRIC URINARY BLADDER TISSUE ENGINEERING

Arun K. Sharma[*,1,2,3] *and Earl Y. Cheng*[1,2,3]
[1]Children's Memorial Hospital of Chicago,
Division of Pediatric Urology; Chicago, IL, US
[2]Northwestern University Feinberg School of Medicine,
Department of Urology, Chicago IL, US
[3]Northwestern University, Institute for BioNanotechnology in Medicine (IBNAM),
Chicago IL, US

RESEARCH SUMMARY

Tissue engineering is a multi-disciplinary field that is continually evolving and functions through the amalgamation of principles and practices derived from materials science, clinical medicine, and the basic biological sciences. The goals of tissue engineering based therapies are to reconstitute the anatomic milieu and physiological function of diseased or damaged tissue in order to improve the poorly functioning target organ with the ultimate end goal to preserve the overall well being of the patient. With the advent of new synthetic polymers and advancements in stem cell biology, the combinatorial and/or synergistic effects of these disciplines has greatly advanced tissue engineering as a whole, particularly in the field of bladder tissue engineering.

Bladder insufficiency caused by trauma or disease including developmental defects are diagnosed each year within the United States. Typical treatment options often include surgery in the form of transurethral resection; segmental or radical cystectomy; or urinary diversion in the case of bladder cancer or enterocystoplasty for those suffering from spina bifida induced neurogenic bladder. Although these are only a few examples that illustrate the more common bladder abnormalities seen by adult and pediatric urologists alike, each of these cases demonstrate suboptimal bladder function due to aberrant cellular behavior and must be

---
[*] Correspondence: Arun K. Sharma, Ph.D., The Feinberg School of Medicine at Northwestern University, Institute for BioNanotechnology in Medicine, 303 East Superior Street, IBNAM 11-113, Chicago, IL 60611 (telephone:312-503-1101; FAX:312-503-1222; e-mail: arun-sharma@northwestern.edu)

restored. Recent clinical bladder tissue engineering studies utilizing autologous cell sources of bladder cells combined with well characterized matrices led to partial restoration of bladder function of patients suffering from myelomeningocele (spina bifida). Although novel in approach, the clinical outcomes of these studies displayed marginal increases in overall bladder function. There is still a clinical need to explore novel biodegradable matrices that can be utilized in conjunction with sources of non-diseased cells that are suitable for bladder regenerative studies. This chapter will focus on the current state of bladder tissue engineering with a specific emphasis on the use of autologous and allogenic cell sources as well as biologic and synthetic matrices that influence cell growth and differentiation that can be used for future bladder tissue engineering applications.

In: Materials Science Researcher Biographical Sketches …   ISBN: 978-1-61942-153-0
Editors: Satomi Matsumoto and Ueda Iwate   © 2013 Nova Science Publishers, Inc.

Chapter 99

CHITOSAN FROM AQUATIC AND TERRESTRIAL ORGANISMS AND MICROORGANISMS: PRODUCTION, PROPERTIES AND APPLICATIONS

Nitar Nwe*, Tetsuya Furuike and Hiroshi Tamura†
Faculty of Chemistry, Materials and Bioengineering,
Kansai University, Suita, Osaka, Japan

RESEARCH SUMMARY

Natural polymers, chitin and chitosan are found as supporting materials in many aquatic organisms, in many insects, in terrestrial crustaceans, in mushrooms and in some fungi. Nowadays, commercially chitin and chitosan are produced from shells of shrimps and crabs and bone plates of squids. Chitosan is non-toxic, biocompatible and biodegradable. It has been used to prepare various forms: powder, solution, hydrogel, membrane, fiber, macro- and micro-beads and scaffold. Based on these properties, chitosan has been tested and used in A-Z applications: antioxidative agent to zinc removing agent. Here physico-chemical properties of chitosans such as molecular weight, degree of acetylation and solubility are of major importance for success on those applications. In this chapter, advantages and disadvantages of the production of chitosans from aquatic and terrestrial organisms and microorganisms are presented from the viewpoints of raw materials, technologies, solid and liquid waste, research contributions, manufacturing facilities and marketing. Moreover the properties and applications of chitosans from those sources are also presented from the viewpoint of relationship between properties of chitosans and applications of chitosans.

---

* E.mail: nitarnwe@yahoo.com (N.N), Tel: +81-6-6368-0871, Fax: +81-6-6330-3770.
† E.mail: tamura@kansai-u.ac.jp (H.T), Tel: +81-6-6368-0871, Fax: +81-6-6330-3770.

In: Materials Science Researcher Biographical Sketches ...   ISBN: 978-1-61942-153-0
Editors: Satomi Matsumoto and Ueda Iwate   © 2013 Nova Science Publishers, Inc.

Chapter 100

DEGRADATION PARAMETERS AND MECHANICAL PROPERTIES EVOLUTION

Andre Vieira

Institute of Mechanical Engineering and Industrial Management,
Campus FEUP, Porto, Portugal

RESEARCH SUMMARY

Biodegradable materials find application in many different market segments, from biomedical devices for regenerative medicine and controlled drug release, to commodity products to be disposed by composting. For these last applications, biodegradable plastics claim clear environmental advantages in several brief use applications, mainly in their final stage of life (waste disposal). This can clearly be evident through life cycle assessment. Performance of a device depends of its behaviour to a mechanical, thermal or chemical applied stress. It is mostly conditioned by the materials selection and dimensioning of the product. For a biodegradable product, contrarily to other products, performance is supposed to decrease along its degradation. From the final user point of view, performance should be enough for the predicted use, during all its life cycle. Biodegradable plastics can present short term performances similar to conventional plastics. There are many biodegradable polymers commercially available to produce a great variety of plastic products, each of them with suitable properties according to the application. However the design process is slight more complex. It must contemplate besides the mechanical stress degradation, also defined as the time-dependent cumulative irreversible damage, the degradation due to hydrolysis. In this chapter, important considerations will be elucidated about biodegradable product design, in the phase of material selection and dimensioning.

In: Materials Science Researcher Biographical Sketches ...   ISBN: 978-1-61942-153-0
Editors: Satomi Matsumoto and Ueda Iwate   © 2013Nova Science Publishers, Inc.

Chapter 101

POLY LACTIC ACID: AN ENVIRONMENTALLY FRIENDLY BIODEGRADABLE POLYMER

Rojan P. John[1], G. S. Anisha[2], Nimisha R. Nair[3] and K. M. Nampoothiri[3]

[1]Institut national de la recherche scientifique-Eau Terre Environnement, Quebec, Canada
[2]Department of Zoology, Government College, Chittur, Palakkad, India
[3]Biotechnology Division, National Institute for Interdisciplinary Science and Technology, (NIIST), CSIR, Trivandrum, India

RESEARCH SUMMARY

Increased concern over environmental pollution caused by synthetic plastics has forced the researchers to develop biodegradable plastics like polylactic acid (PLA). PLA is a thermoplastic with a reasonable shelf-life and can be used to yield articles for single-use packaging such as bottles, food wrappers, fibers for clothing and in biomedical applications, such as for sutures, prosthetic materials and materials for drug delivery. It can be made from annually renewable resources and, when disposed of properly, will hydrolyze to harmless natural products. PLA is a polymer in which the stereochemical structure can easily be modified by polymerizing a controlled mixture of the L- or D-isomers to yield high molecular weight amorphous or crystalline polymers that can be used for food contact and are generally recognized as safe (GRAS).

The basic building block for PLA is lactic acid. Lactic acid can be manufactured either by carbohydrate fermentation or chemical synthesis, of which fermentation predominates. The majority of the world`s commercially produced lactic acid is made by the bacterial fermentation of carbohydrates, using homolactic organisms such as various optimized or modified strains of the genus *Lactobacillus*, which exclusively form lactic acid. Different pure carbohydrates and wastes generated from agro-industries can be utilized as raw material for lactic acid fermentation by bacteria such as, *Lactobacillus* spp. and fungi, such as

Rhizopus sp. Ring-opening polymerization of lactide, the dimer of lactic acid is considered as the efficient method for synthesis of PLA. PLA could be a technical and economic solution to the problem of eventual disposal of very large amount of plastic packaging worldwide.

In: Materials Science Researcher Biographical Sketches ...   ISBN: 978-1-61942-153-0
Editors: Satomi Matsumoto and Ueda Iwate   © 2013 Nova Science Publishers, Inc.

Chapter 102

BIODEGRADABLE MATERIALS: A GREENER TECHNOLOGY FOR WATER PURIFICATION

*Shivani B. Mishra**

Department of Chemical Technology, University of Johannesburg,
Johannesburg, South Africa

RESEARCH SUMMARY

Existence of safe water for the planet earth and its inhabitants is an issue that always needs an improved technology to keep safe our environment for future generations. The safe water is under serious threat due to non-stop increase in pollution by industries, sewage, atmospheric deposition, oil pollution, radioactive wastes and global warming. Across the world, the investigation to use a greener approach for water purification is one of the thrust areas. Biodegradable materials play a huge role towards keeping the water clean. This chapter focuses on the research and development made in this direction where biodegradable materials have been used to develop an ecofriendly technology for water purification.

* Author for correspondence: Ph.: +27-11-559-6163, Fax: +27-11-559-6425, E.mail:smishra@uj.ac.za, Department of Chemical Technology, University of Johannesburg, P.O. Box 17011, Doornfontein 2028, Johannesburg, South Africa.

In: Materials Science Researcher Biographical Sketches ...   ISBN: 978-1-61942-153-0
Editors: Satomi Matsumoto and Ueda Iwate   © 2013 Nova Science Publishers, Inc.

Chapter 103

FUNCTIONAL PROPERTIES OF BIOPOLYMERS FOR DRUG DELIVERY APPLICATIONS

Philip F. Builders[*,1] *and Anthony A. Attama*[2]

[1]Department of Pharmaceutical Technology and Raw Material Development,
National Institute for Pharmaceutical Research and Development, Abuja Nigeria
[2]Department of Pharmaceutics, Faculty of Pharmaceutical Sciences,
University of Nigeria Nsukka, Enugu State, Nigeria

RESEARCH SUMMARY

Biopolymers are polymers of natural origin. They are derived either directly from biological systems or are chemically synthesized from basic biological building blocks. The use of biopolymers for drug delivery has been made attractive because of their functional versatility, biodegradability and biocompatibility. Besides being available on a sustainable basis, biopolymers have several other functional, economic and environmental advantages that make them overtly desirable. The applications of biopolymers in drug delivery systems offer conceptual models for improving the efficacy of existing drug formulations and developing new therapy regimens. This class of polymers has successfully been used in therapeutics (polymer therapeutics) and as platforms for effective delivery of medicines and therapeutic genes by innovative formulations using appropriate technology. The frequently used biopolymers for drug delivery applications are mostly polysaccharides such as starch, chitosan, cellulose, gums and mucilages together with their synthetic and semi-synthetic derivatives. Peptides and polynucleotides are emerging as new class of biopolymers due to their unique chemical, physical and biological properties. The development of polynucleotides and peptide-based polymers for drug delivery is driven by the convergence of protein engineering and macromolecular self-assembly. The application of biopolymers in novel site-specific drug delivery systems and delivery of challenging small molecule drugs and biotech molecules such as biological response modifiers are essentially due to their individual specific intrinsic properties. Biopolymers remain a large class of biomaterials with

---

[*] Author for correspondence: Email: philsonsky@yahoo.com

a wide variety of unique intrinsic physicochemical and functional properties which make them occupy critical position in drug formulation and delivery. Functional versatility, biocompatibility, biodegradability, wide intrinsic physicochemical properties such as crystalline/amorphous constitution, solution characteristics, swelling and pH responsiveness, viscosity, bioadhesiveness, and excellent compression ability, are among the properties that make biopolymers relevant for use in drug delivery. This review will focus on these main properties of biopolymers.

Chapter 104

BIODEGRADABLE HYDROGELS AS DRUG DELIVERY SYSTEMS FOR TISSUE ENGINEERING APPLICATIONS[*]

Kacey G. Marra[1-4] *and Alicia J. DeFail*[2]

[1]Division of Plastic and Reconstructive Surgery, University of Pittsburgh, Pittsburgh, PA, US
[2]Department of Bioengineering, University of Pittsburgh, Pittsburgh, P PA, US
[3]Department of Surgery, University of Pittsburgh, Pittsburgh, PA, US
[4]McGowan Institute for Regenerative Medicine, Pittsburgh, PA, US

RESEARCH SUMMARY

Tissue engineering is a potential therapeutic strategy which combines scaffolds, cells, and/or growth factors that provide a suitable environment to direct the growth of new, healthy tissue. Scaffolds that are biodegradable, biocompatible, mechanically support tissue growth, and can be shaped to fill an irregularly shaped defect are ideal. Polymeric poly(lactic-*co*-glycolic acid) (PLGA) biomaterials are among the most widely studied tissue-engineered scaffolds. However, polymeric hydrogels, such as poly(ethylene glycol) (PEG) are also being examined as drug delivery scaffolds. Delivery of drugs or growth factors from these scaffolds is desirable to enhance tissue regeneration. The delivery of drugs or growth factors can be controlled by various parameters such as drug loading, polymer composition, and processing techniques. Drugs can also be encapsulated in microspheres or nanospheres for controlled delivery. Other methods of delivery include adsorption of drugs or growth factors to the surface prior to implantation or incorporation during the scaffold fabrication process. The incorporation of microspheres within PLGA scaffolds, fibrin scaffolds, gelatin scaffolds, and poly(ethylene glycol)-based hydrogels is also an option. This chapter describes several of these approaches that results in a controlled, localized release of drugs from the biomaterials. Clinical applications that will be discussed include bone regeneration, breast cancer adjuvant therapies, and nerve regeneration.

---

[*] A version of this chapter also appears in Advances in Condensed Matter and Materials Research, Volume 7, edited by Hans Geelvinck and Sjaak Reynst, published by Nova Science Publishers, Inc. It was submitted for appropriate modifications in an effort to encourage wider dissemination of research.

In: Materials Science Researcher Biographical Sketches ...   ISBN: 978-1-61942-153-0
Editors: Satomi Matsumoto and Ueda Iwate   © 2013 Nova Science Publishers, Inc.

Chapter 105

POLYHYDROXYALKANOATES: A NEW GENERATION OF BIOTECHNOLOGICALLY PRODUCED BIODEGRADABLE POLYMERS[*]

Ipsita Roy and Sheryl Philip
University of Westminster, UK

RESEARCH SUMMARY

Polyhydroxyalkanoates (PHAs) are a family of poly-β-hydroxyesters of 3-, 4-, 5- and 6-hydroxyalkanoic acids, produced by a variety of bacterial species under nutrient-limiting conditions with excess carbon. These water-insoluble storage polymers are biodegradable, exhibit thermoplastic properties and can be produced from renewable carbon sources. Hence, these polymers have the potential to replace the petrochemical-based plastics. In addition, PHAs are also known to be biocompatible and hence have the potential to be utilised for a range of biomedical applications.

PHAs are synthesised by a wide variety of bacteria, both Gram negative and Gram positive such as *Pseudomonas, Bacillus, Ralstonia, Aeromonas, Rhodobacter* and certain Archaea, such as members of the Halobacticeae. There are two main types of PHAs, short chain length PHAs that have C_3-C_5 hydroxyacids as monomers and medium chain length PHAs that have C_6-C_{16} hydroxyacids as monomers. The mechanical properties of these PHAs vary from being quite brittle to extremely elastomeric.

Microbial PHA biosynthesis is carried out by the PHA synthase enzyme that catalyses the stereo-selective conversion of (R)-3-hydroxyacyl-CoA substrates to PHAs with the concomitant release of CoA. Based on their primary structures, substrate specificities of the enzymes and the subunit composition, PHA synthases have been classified into four major classes. It is crucial to understand the mechanism of these enzymes in order to develop better polymer production strategies.

---

[*] A version of this chapter also appears in Biotechnology: Research, Technology and Applications, edited by Felix W. Richter, published by Nova Science Publishers, Inc. It was submitted for appropriate modifications in an effort to encourage wider dissemination of research.

There is considerable interest in the commercial exploitation of these biodegradable polyesters. PHAs can be used for a range of different applications such as tissue engineering, drug delivery, and production of medical devices such as urological stents, in the packaging industry, dye industry, textile industry, for manufacturing adhesives, coatings and moulded goods. In addition, all of the monomeric units of PHAs are enantiomerically pure and in R-configuration. R-hydroxyalkanoic acids produced by the hydrolysis of PHAs can be used as chiral starting materials in fine chemical, pharmaceutical and medical industries. The market value of these polymers is estimated to be about £300 billion annually.

In this chapter we will cover information regarding the various facets of polyhydroxy-alkanoates and trace the evolution of these microbially produced biodegradable polymers as 'new' materials. This information will also include the research findings of our laboratory.

In: Materials Science Researcher Biographical Sketches ...   ISBN: 978-1-61942-153-0
Editors: Satomi Matsumoto and Ueda Iwate   © 2013 Nova Science Publishers, Inc.

Chapter 106

SURFACE MODIFICATION OF ULTRA HIGH MODULUS POLYMERIC FIBERS: EFFECTS ON INTERFACIAL ADHESION AND MECHANICAL PROPERTIES OF EPOXY RESIN COMPOSITES

Petroula A. Tarantili

Polymer Technology Lab., School of Chemical Engineering,
National Technical Univ. of Athens, Athens, Greece

RESEARCH SUMMARY

Surface treatments of aramid fibers by methacryloyl chloride/carbon tetrachloride solution, hydrolysis with sodium hydroxide solution and coating with phenolic polymers, such as resole and novolac resins, were performed in an attempt to improve the adhesive bonding of those fibers with epoxy resin matrices. The modified aramid fibers were subsequently used for preparation of composite materials with epoxy matrix. The mechanical properties of these composites were investigated and the results explained taking into consideration the surface characteristics of modified fibers, as determined by pull-out tests and contact angle measurements. Treatment of aramids with methacryloyl chloride was found an interesting modification for subsequent use of those fibers as reinforcement in epoxy matrices. Flexural properties of the above composites are significantly improved and the obvious effect on the fiber surface is a change in morphology. Coating of aramid fibers with phenolic resins seemed adequate to promote interfacial adhesive bonding to epoxy matrices, due to the changes in fiber surface profile, the affinity with the aramid substrate and the chemical reactivity to the epoxy resin.

In the context of the above research, corona and chromate surface-treated UHMPE fibers, as well as calendered fibers were used as reinforcement for epoxy resins and the obtained composites were investigated for their mechanical properties as a function of the fiber morphology and characteristics. The treated fibers were tested by scanning electron microscopy (SEM), tensile and pull-out testing as well as contact angle measurements. Mechanical tests, such as flexural and interlaminar shear strength (ILSS), have also been performed with unidirectional specimens reinforced with the above fibers. The results showed that corona and chromate treated fibers give the highest adhesive bonding, whereas their tensile strength is reduced. The same is also observed with the flexural tests, where maximum strength corresponds to these two types of fibers for various filler volume fractions. Finally, the data derived from ILLS suggest a slight advantage for the corona treated fibers.

Regarding the performance of treated UHMPE fibers it was shown that corona and chromate treatments modify their surface and give products with reduced strength, but lead to increased adhesive bonding. On the other hand, calendered fibers retain their strength with significant reduction of modulus due to some relaxation during hot calendaring. Properties dependent on the off-axis properties of the composite specimens, such as flexural and interlaminar shear strength, showed that corona treated fibers are advantageous as reinforcement for epoxies.

In: Materials Science Researcher Biographical Sketches …   ISBN: 978-1-61942-153-0
Editors: Satomi Matsumoto and Ueda Iwate   © 2013 Nova Science Publishers, Inc.

Chapter 107

MANUFACTURING AND FEATURES OF ACOUSTICALLY OPTIMIZED NATURAL FIBRE REINFORCED PLASTICS

N. Aisenbrey and L. Frormann

Institut für Produktionstechnik,
Westsächsische Hochschule Zwickau, Germany

RESEARCH SUMMARY

Fibre reinforced plastics are used worldwide in various applications. Large quantities of natural fibre reinforced plastics are processed in the automobile industry due to their good mechanical and ecological characteristics, but particularly because of their low price. The application range is mainly in low loaded places, e.g., in the inside of automobiles like the side door panels or ceiling. Initially the market for natural fibres showed a rapid upswing that stagnated afterwards due to their limited range of applications. To force the application, supplementary functions must be integrated into the materials with no additional costs. Usually the focus of the research is on the increase of the mechanical characteristic values and the development of more economical and productive manufacturing methods. The high acoustic potential of the natural fibres is less investigated and only considered as a side effect. But this acoustic potential enables many application possibilities of the reinforced plastics. Particularly, the health endangerment by the constant increase of the noise pollution clarifies the necessity for the research. Acoustically effective structural elements can be manufactured as a sandwich. The building method of a sandwich element permits a large variation range. With simple changes in the structure, for example by the use of different layers with different characteristics, the material can be adapted to several applications. An effective sound absorption particularly in the middle and high frequency ranges is possible with layers of natural fibre nonwovens or open porous natural fibre reinforced plastics. Sound absorption values over 0.7 are reached at frequencies above 1 kHz. High weighted difference level D_w values of up to 30 dB can be achieved with very thin natural fibre reinforced composite plates, which exceed the mass law up to 4 dB. The sound absorption achievement of multilayered elements with firm surface layers and different core materials is very good with weighted difference level values of 34–37 dB with low element weights between 13–16 kg/m². For these high strength lightweight construction units with positive acoustic characteristics in sound insulation and sound absorption, various applications exist in the architectural acoustics and in the automobile industry. The application of natural fibre reinforced elements as multi functional wall and ceiling panels permits a strong stimulation of the market for these materials.

In: Materials Science Researcher Biographical Sketches ...   ISBN: 978-1-61942-153-0
Editors: Satomi Matsumoto and Ueda Iwate   © 2013 Nova Science Publishers, Inc.

Chapter 108

EFFECTS OF MICROSTRUCTURE ON RESIDUAL STRESSES IN DSE AL₂O₃/YAG CERAMIC COMPOSITE BY EXPERIMENTAL AND NUMERICAL INVESTIGATIONS

J. J. Sha[1,2,] S. Ochiai[3], H. Okuda[3], S. Iwamoto[3],
K. Morishita[3], Y. Waku[4], N. Nakagawa[4], A. Mitani[4],
T. Ishikawa[4] and M. Sato[4]*

[1]State Key Lab. of Structural Analyses for Industrial Equipment, Dalian University of Technology, Dalian, China
[2]Ceramic Materials Engineering, University of Bayreuth, Bayreuth, Germany
[3]Department of Materials Science and Engineering, Kyoto University, Kyoto, Japan
[4]Ube Industries Ltd., Ube, Yamaguchi, Japan

RESEARCH SUMMARY

The effect of microstructure on the residual stresses in directionally solidified eutectic (DSE) $Al_2O_3/Y_3Al_5O_{12}$ (YAG) ceramic composite were investigated by X-ray diffraction technique and finite element method (FEM).

In the X-ray stress measurement, the YAG skeleton derived from the Al_2O_3/YAG composite by dioxidation of the Al_2O_3 phase was used as a reference specimen without thermally-induced stress, and the X-ray stress measurements with CuKα1 irradiation were performed on the two faces of a cubic specimen, namely, the faces parallel and perpendicular to the solidification direction, respectively. On the other hand, a numerical analysis using finite element method (FEM) which represents the actual microstructure features of the experimental specimen was carried out in different local regions with different morphologies to reveal the effect of microstructure on the distribution of residual stress in the composite.

[*] E-mail address: Shajianjun720@yahoo.com.

The distributions of residual stresses in both constituting phases were mapped by FEM calculation. Meanwhile, the mapping of residual stress indicated that the distribution of residual stress in the interior of each phase was not homogeneous being dependent on the solidification direction and local morphologies of constituting phases such as curvature of interfaces, array and volume fraction. The experimentally measured residual stresses were accounted for by the FEM analysis.

In: Materials Science Researcher Biographical Sketches ...   ISBN: 978-1-61942-153-0
Editors: Satomi Matsumoto and Ueda Iwate   © 2013 Nova Science Publishers, Inc.

Chapter 109

INTRODUCTION OF PARTICLE DISPERSION REINFORCED CERAMIC MATRIX COMPOSITES

*Bin Li[1,2,]**, *Jianxin Deng*[2] *and Hong Wang*[3]
[1]Department of Mechanical Engineering,
Luoyang Institute of Science and Technology, Henan Province, PR China
[2]School of Mechanical Engineering,
Shandong University, Shandong Province, PR China
[3]Luoyang Institute of Science and Technology, Luoyang Henan Province, PR China

RESEARCH SUMMARY

The study of brittle material mechanics is still a young and living science. Even now, the making of ceramic pieces for use in mechanical design, that are subjected to dimensional tolerances similar to those used for steel, or of complex geometry, gives rise to difficult problems, which hinder the large scale development of these materials, despite their extraordinary intrinsic properties. Particle dispersion reinforcing is an important way to improve the performance of ceramic matrix composites. In this chapture, fabrication processes of particle reinforced ceramic are introduced, which provide a useful set of variables for model experimental and theoretical studies. Toughening mechanisms of particle dispersion reinforced ceramic matrix composites are also discussed. When the second phase is added into the matrix, usually there existe the mismatch of structural, mechanical or physical properties, the mismatches of linear expansion coefficient and elastic modulus are related to the toughening and strengthening of ceramic. Meanwhile, the practice of the composites containing the latest research results is also introduced.

---

* E-mail address: libinman@gmail.com (B. Li).

In: Materials Science Researcher Biographical Sketches …   ISBN: 978-1-61942-153-0

Editors: Satomi Matsumoto and Ueda Iwate   © 2013 Nova Science Publishers, Inc.

Chapter 110

A NOVEL STRATEGY FOR DEVELOPING POLYMER NANOCOMPOSITE WITH HIGH DIELECTRIC CONSTANT

Jing-Wen Wang and Shu-Qin Li

Department of Material Science and Engineering,
College of Material Science and Technology,
Nanjing University of Aeronautics and Astronautics, Nanjing, P. R. China

RESEARCH SUMMARY

A novel nanofabrication strategy to develop high dielectric constant nanocomposite was introduced using poly(vinylidene fluoride) (a piezoelectric polymer) as matrix and PCMS-g-CuPc [poly(p-chloromethyl styrene) (PCMS) grafted with copper phthalocyanine oligomer (CuPc, a planar multiring organic semiconductor with super high dielectric constant more than 10^5)] as filler. Improvement of the dispersibility of CuPc oligomer in polymer matrix was confirmed by TEM-observed morphologies. The PCMS-g-CuPc particles with a average size of about 80nm are dispersed in poly(vinylidene fluoride) matrix, while in PCMS-g-CuPc particles the PCMS acts as "matrix" which contains dispersed CuPc balls with a average size of ca. 25nm [about 1/20 of that of CuPc particles in the simple blend of poly(vinylidene fluoride) and CuPc]. The slution-cast nanocomposite film sample with only 15wt% CuPc can realize a dielectric constant of about 325 at 100Hz, more than 38-fold enhancement with respect to that of the pure PVDF. The enhanced dielectric response in the nanocomposite demonstrates the significance of the interface effect in raising the material responses far beyond that expected by simple mixing rules when there is a large dielectric contrast between the two components in the composite. Theoretic prediction using modified Cole-Cole equation indicates that, even at the high frequency limit, the dielectric constant of the nanocomposite can still be more than 70. Furthermore, the dielectric strength increase from 40 MV/m of the simple physical blend of poly(vinylidene fluoride) and CuPc to 51 MV/m of the nanocomposite sample. All these will lead to a nanocomposite with better controlled process conditions and are highly desirable for high dielectric constant composites.

In: Materials Science Researcher Biographical Sketches ...   ISBN: 978-1-61942-153-0
Editors: Satomi Matsumoto and Ueda Iwate   © 2013 Nova Science Publishers, Inc.

Chapter 111

POLYMER MATRIX COMPOSITES: PROPERTIES, PERFORMANCE AND APPLICATIONS

Milan Kracalik, Stephan Laske and Clemens Holzer
Institute of Plastics Processing, University of Leoben, Leoben, Austria

RESEARCH SUMMARY

Preparation of polymer-clay nanocomposites by melt mixing has been intensively investigated in the last 20 years. However, only systems based on polyamide matrix have been commercialized. The problem consists mostly in question how to up-scale the results obtained using laboratory equipment. Most of research institutions dealing with nanocomposites compounding are equipped by "micro" twin screw extruders, which are able to process only small amount (in order of grams per hour) of material. In the industry, compounding throughput in order of kilograms up to tonnes per hour is usual. However, industrial compounders are normally not available for research purpose. Furthermore, the broad range of industrial compounders (differences in screw geometry, screw diameter, L/D relation etc.) makes any general conclusions impossible. In this contribution, approach for systematic investigation of polymer nanocomposites is presented. A way from "micro" to "advanced" compounding using laboratory as well as semi-industrial twin screw extruders is described.

In: Materials Science Researcher Biographical Sketches …   ISBN: 978-1-61942-153-0
Editors: Satomi Matsumoto and Ueda Iwate   © 2013 Nova Science Publishers, Inc.

Chapter 112

CONTACT STRENGTH OF CERAMIC MATERIALS

Lucia Hegedusova, Ladislav Ceniga[*]*and Jan Dusza*
Institute of Materials Research, Slovak Academy of Sciences,
Kosice, Slovak Republic

RESEARCH SUMMARY

This chapter deals with the determination of strength of ceramic materials by mechanical tests in bending and contact modes, and subsequently with nanostructural and microstructural analyses of strength-degrading defects. The bending and contact modes are simulated by a four-point bending test and a single-cycle contact tests using rollers or a single/multicontact test using spheres, respectively. Additionally, a combination of the multi-contact test using spheres and the four-point bending test as well as contact fatigue test, i.e. the multi-cycle contact test using spheres to be performed till material failure, are also considered. In general, the determination of strength of ceramic materials results from statistical methods, usually represented by the Weibull analysis to result in the determination of the characteristic strength σ_o and the Weibull modulus m. Accordingly, the characteristic strength $\sigma_{o,bend}$ and $\sigma_{o,cont}$ as well as the Weibull moduli m$bend$ and m$cont$, related to the four-point bending test and the single-cycle contact test using rollers, respectively, are determined along with the determination of an experimental relationships between $\sigma_{o,bend}$, $\sigma_{o,cont}$ and an experimental relationship between m$_{bend}$, m$_{cont}$, Weibull parameters _0,cont, mcont of the single-cycle contact test using spheres and _0,bend, mbend can be defined.

Strength of ceramic materials determined by the four-point bending test and the single-cycle contact test using rollers is assumed to be influenced by the presence of the processing flaws in a form of pores to represent fracture origins. Additionally, the contact mode performed by rollers induces different types of cracks, i.e. lateral, median and contact end cracks, in contrast to the contact mode performed by spheres to induce cone cracks being assumed to be a reason of material failure except of the ceramic materials to exhibit a quasi-plastic character in compression, where median cracks are initiated and propagated regardless the contact mode performed by spheres. Stable growth of the cone cracks is assumed to be a

---

[*] E-mail addresses: lceniga@yahoo.com, lceniga@hotmail.com.

reason of higher values of m*cont* compared with lower ones of m*bend*. Accordingly, the higher values of m*cont* correspond to significant preciseness within the determination of strength of ceramic materials by the single-cycle contact test using spheres to exhibit additionally higher values of $\sigma_{o,cont}$ compared with those of the four-point bending test and the single-cycle contact test using rollers. Finally, the contact test performed by spheres thus enables to obtain reproducible results, and is suitable for the determination of contact strength. On the one hand, the determination requires large amount of specimens but, on the other hand, the specimens are of small dimensions what is an advantage of this experimental technique to be accordingly suitable for new developed ceramic materials.

In: Materials Science Researcher Biographical Sketches …   ISBN: 978-1-61942-153-0
Editors: Satomi Matsumoto and Ueda Iwate   © 2013 Nova Science Publishers, Inc.

Chapter 113

NEW ANALYTICAL MODEL OF THERMAL STRESSES AND ANALYTICAL FRACTUREMECHANICS IN TWO-COMPONENT MATERIALS. APPLICATION TO TWO-COMPONENT CERAMICS

Ladislav Ceniga[*]

Institute of Materials Research, Slovak Academy of Sciences,
Kosice, Slovak Republic

RESEARCH SUMMARY

The chapter deals with a new analytical model of thermal stresses in an isotropic continuum represented by periodically distributed isotropic spherical particles in an isotropic infinite matrix. The multi-particlematrix system to represent a model system regarding the analytical modelling is applicable to a two-component material of a precipitate-matrix type, consisted of isotropic components. The thermal stresses as functions of microstructural parameters (particle volume fraction, particle radius, inter-particle distance) originate during a cooling process as a consequence of the difference in thermal expansion coefficients. Additionally, integrals of elastic energy density along curves in the spherical particles and the matrix are derived to result in the determination of a critical particle radius as a consequence of the initiation of cracks in the components of any two-component material (ductile, brittle) along with the determination of functions describing the crack shapes in a plane perpendicular to a direction of the crack propagation in an ideal-brittle particle and an ideal-brittle matrix. With regard to the ideal-brittle particle and the idealbrittle matrix resulting in an application of the presented results to ceramic (brittle) components, the new analytical model, and consequently an analysis of the crack initiation and the crack propagation are applied to the SiC-Si3N4 and SiC-MoSi2 multi-particle-matrix systems representing two-component ceramic materials of the precipitate-matrix type.

---

[*] E-mail addresses: lceniga@yahoo.com, lceniga@hotmail.com.

In: Materials Science Researcher Biographical Sketches ...   ISBN: 978-1-61942-153-0
Editors: Satomi Matsumoto and Ueda Iwate   © 2013 Nova Science Publishers, Inc.

Chapter 114

FINITE ELEMENT THERMAL ANALYSIS OF CERAMICS MATRIX COMPOSITES

M. A. Sheikh[*]

School of Mechanical, Aerospace and Civil Engineering
The University of Manchester, Sackville Street Building
Manchester, United Kingdom

RESEARCH SUMMARY

Modelling and analysis of a unique geometrically representative Unit Cell has been shown here as the key to predicting the macro thermal transport behaviour of composites, which otherwise requires the employment of a vast experimental infrastructure. Sophisticated materials, such as woven Ceramic Matrix Composites (CMCs), have very complex and expensive manufacturing routes, used by just a few research organizations. This broadens the scope of a modelling strategy to be adopted for the characterization of all possible material designs with various possible constituent volume fractions by using a commercial FE code such as ABAQUS. The variation of material constituents can be incorporated in the Unit Cell model geometry with subtle manipulation of key parameters dictated by quantitative SEM morphological data. Two CMC material systems have been modeled in the present study. The first material has been analysed with a focus on the homogenization of microscopic constituent material properties into the macroscopic thermal transport character. The actual set of property data used for the Unit Cell of this material is obtained from the cumulative property degradation results extracted from the analyses of three sub-models based on the material's unique porosity data. After validating the modeling methodology through a comparison with the experimental data, a geometrically more challenging CMC is modelled with a detailed incorporation of its morphological complexity in order to predict its macroscopic thermal transport behavior. Finally, it is shown how these models can be more efficiently analysed in a multi-processing parallel environment.

---

[*] E-mail address: m.sheikh@manchester.ac.uk. Tel: +44 (0) 161 306 3802; Fax: +44 (0) 161 306 3803.

In: Materials Science Researcher Biographical Sketches …   ISBN: 978-1-61942-153-0
Editors: Satomi Matsumoto and Ueda Iwate   © 2013 Nova Science Publishers, Inc.

Chapter 115

DAMAGE REDUCTION METHODS IN DRILLING POLYMERIC MATRIX COMPOSITES

A. Di Ilio and A. Paoletti*

DIMEG, University of L'Aquila, L'Aquila, Italy

RESEARCH SUMMARY

Drilling of polymeric matrix composites may generate several kinds of damage, which can lead to unacceptable material degradation. The aim of this chapter is to present a literature review on the principal methods adopted to enhance holes quality. The major damage is certainly the delamination that can occur both on the entry and exit sides of the workpiece. The level of delamination is related to a critical thrust force value which is dependent on the workpiece material and the uncut layer from the main body of the laminate.

* E-mail address: diilio@ing.univaq.it (Corresponding author)

In: Materials Science Researcher Biographical Sketches …   ISBN: 978-1-61942-153-0
Editors: Satomi Matsumoto and Ueda Iwate   © 2013 Nova Science Publishers, Inc.

Chapter 116

RECENT ADVANCES IN THE ANALYSIS OF VETERINARY DRUGS AND GROWTH-PROMOTING AGENTS BY CHROMATOGRAPHIC TECHNIQUES

A. Garrido Frenich, P. Plaza-Bolaños, M. M. Aguilera-Luiz and J. L. Martínez-Vidal*

Research Group "Analytical Chemistry of Contaminants",
Department of Analytical Chemistry, Almeria University, Almeria, Spain

RESEARCH SUMMARY

Antibiotics have been mainly used in veterinary practices and they are frequently found in food, environmental and biological matrices. Microbiological methods have been traditionally applied because they are easy to perform and are inexpensive. However they do not distinguish among several classes of veterinary drugs and they only provide semi-quantitative analysis, and sometimes give rise to false positives. They are still used due to their simplicity although they have been replaced with chromatographic and electrophoretic techniques, which allow simultaneous determination of several classes of veterinary drugs. In this sense, liquid chromatography (LC) coupled to several detectors is currently widely used and it is a reference technique for the determination of these type of compounds, even replacing gas chromatography (GC), due to they are rather polar, non-volatile and thermolabile compounds.

Although LC has been coupled to conventional detectors such as fluorescence, UV-visible or diode array (DAD), in the last few years, mass spectrometry (MS) has been widely used, due to this type of detection provides more reliable identification and confirmation of these analytes than conventional detectors. Basically, triple quadrupole (QqQ) and time-of-flight (TOF) analyzers have been mainly used for the determination of veterinary drugs, because confirmation and quantification are included in the same step, although in the last few years an hybrid analyzer, the quadrupole-time-of-flight (Q-TOF) has been an emerging

---

* E-mail: agarrido@ual.es.

analyzer to be coupled to LC for accurate mass measurement and unequivocal identification of veterinary drug residues and their metabolites.

However, one of the main problems associated with LC methods is the time consumed during the chromatographic analysis. The use of ultra performance liquid chromatography (UPLC) has become very popular in the last few years. This approach is based on the reduction of the particle size of the stationary phase (< 2 µm), and it allows a decrease in analysis time and an increase in sensitivity.

This survey describes the most relevant information related to the chromatographic determination of veterinary drug residues in food, environmental and biological samples, providing the main applications performed in this type of matrices, as well as the main advances related to the chromatographic techniques.

In: Materials Science Researcher Biographical Sketches ...   ISBN: 978-1-61942-153-0
Editors: Satomi Matsumoto and Ueda Iwate   © 2013 Nova Science Publishers, Inc.

Chapter 117

HPLC: THE DOMINANT SEPARATION TECHNIQUE WITH A WIDE RANGE OF APPLICATIONS

Victoria F. Samanidou and Ioannis N. Papadoyannis*

Laboratory of Analytical Chemistry, Department of Chemistry,
Aristotle University of Thessaloniki, Thessaloniki, Greece

RESEARCH SUMMARY

Chromatography is a science that counts more than one century, since its introduction, but in recent years has expanded exponentially because of the availability of advanced tecnhiques to be applied for the analysis of innumerous analytes in a very wide variety of matrices.

In principle chromatographic techniques belong to separation science.

Separation is achieved by regulating the magnitude of the distribution coefficient between two distinguished phases: one stationary and one mobile. As the components of a mixture migrate with different rates due to their different distribution coefficients they separate. Depending on the type of these phases there are several chromatographic techniques. When the mobile phase is a liquid, the chromatography is called liquid chromate-graphy. The most sophisticated type of liquid chromatography is HPLC where the mobile phase runs through the stationary by means of a pump at elevated pressures.

HPLC has been used in an extremely wide range of analytical methods and it is impossible to give a comprehensive set of examples that would illustrate its wide applicability in a variety of matrices. This chapter summarises a few LC analyses that may indicate the scope of the use of HPLC in the analysis of a variety of samples in several scientific fields giving just a tiny idea of the power, the versatility and the superbness of this technique.

* Tel:+30231997698, FAX: +302310997719, e-mail: samanidu@chem.auth.gr.

Examples described in the following paragraphs include the method development for the separation of several analytes in a broad range of matrices involved in:

- Clinical analysis: such as aminoacids, water and fat soluble vitamins in biological fluids, caffeine metabolism products: methylxanthines and methyluric acids in human biological fluids, iodotyrosines and iodothyronines in biological samples, methadone and its main metabolite EDDP in biological fluids, 1,4 benzodiazepines and tricyclic antidepressants in human biological fluids etc.

- Food analysis: such as free phenolic acids in wines and wine vinegar, fluoroquinolones, penicillins, sulphonamides, cephalosporins and tetracyclines residues in tissues of various food producing animals, and products like milk, eggs, and muscle tissues.

- Veterinary medicine: such as the analysis of different veterinary drugs in commercial products and blood samples as well.

- Pharmaceutical analysis: such as antibiotics, vitamins, antidepressants, etc in pharmaceutical formulations for human and veterinary medicine.

- Environmental analysis: such as the monitoring of different pollutants like anthracene and its oxidation products in surface waters, carbamate pesticides, chlorophenols, silver iodide, different ions in drinking water as well as in surface waters

- Environmental technology: such as the study of pollution reduction using novel sorbent materials by means of the determination of residual ions.

- Forensic science: such as the analysis of ballpoint pen ink components- study of their decomposition on aging.

In: Materials Science Researcher Biographical Sketches …   ISBN: 978-1-61942-153-0
Editors: Satomi Matsumoto and Ueda Iwate   © 2013 Nova Science Publishers, Inc.

Chapter 118

METHODS AND TECHNIQUES FOR THE ANALYSIS OF ISOFLAVONES IN FOODS

M. A. Rostagno[*,1], *N. Manchón*[1], *E. Guillamón*[1], *A. García-Lafuente*[1], *A. Villares*[1] *and J. A. Martínez*[1,2]

[1]Centro para la Calidad de los Alimentos, Instituto Nacional de Investigación y Tecnología Agraria y Alimentaria (INIA), Campus Universitario "Duques de Soria", Soria, Soria, Spain
[2]Universidad de Navarra, Dpto. Fisiología y Nutrición, Edificio de Investigación, Pamplona, Spain

RESEARCH SUMMARY

Soy isoflavones are a phytochemical group of interest due to their possible health protective effects including reducing the risk of cardiovascular disease, lowering rates of prostate, breast and colon cancers, and improving bone health among many other claims. Much attention has been paid to the extraction and analysis of these compounds from foods since exact quantification is required to perform epidemiological studies and to establish their possible role in disease prevention. Unfortunately, analysis of isoflavones is a complicated procedure because there are several factors which may influence results, such as stability, incomplete recoveries during extraction, and difficult chromatographic separation of some chemical forms, among others. In this chapter, several aspects of isoflavone analysis in foods will be discussed, including sample conservation, sample preparation and analysis techniques. Special emphasis will be given to analysis techniques, separation and identification issues as well as the use of new technologies, such as UPLC and monolithic columns. Finally, different analysis protocols for the determination of these compounds in foods are proposed by combining different sample preparation and analysis techniques and methods available in the recent literature.

---

[*] Corresponding author e-mail: rostagno.mauricio@inia.es, Telephone: (+34) 975 233204, Fax: (+34) 975 233205.

In: Materials Science Researcher Biographical Sketches …   ISBN: 978-1-61942-153-0
Editors: Satomi Matsumoto and Ueda Iwate   © 2013 Nova Science Publishers, Inc.

Chapter 119

UPDATE OF THE CARBAMATE, PHENYLUREA AND PHENOXYACID DERIVATIZATION REACTIONS FOR THEIR GAS CHROMATOGRAPHY DETERMINATION

E. Crespo-Corral, M. J. Santos-Delgado and L. M. Polo-Díez
Complutense University of Madrid, Madrid, Spain

RESEARCH SUMMARY

The persistence and toxicity of organochlorine and organophosphorus herbicides justify their replacement by other more easily degradable ones, such as phenoxy-acids, carbamates and phenylureas; however, the widespread use of these herbicides in agriculture and gardening has increased their presence in the environment, as well as that of their metabolites some of which are more toxic than the original herbicides. This has lead to the development of sensitive methods for their determination. In general terms, Gas Chromatography, GC, is a very sensitive technique widely used for residue analysis with volatile and thermostable compounds. However, the above mentioned compounds are quite polar and/or thermo-sensitive and they require derivatization. Although some carbamates and phenylureas could be directly determined by GC using controlled conditions, simultaneous direct analysis of several families with very different polarity would require programmed temperatures, which makes the use of gentle chromatographic conditions difficult.

Among the different esterification reactions available for phenoxy acids the one based on the use of diazomethane, whose hazardous properties are well known, is proposed in the 8150 EPA Method. On the other hand, the most often used derivatization reaction for carbamate and phenylurea herbicides is based on alkylation with NaH/DMSO/MeI, which has the disadvantage of NaH′s virulent reaction with water. The use of a closed laboratory-made glass reactor can minimize risks involved, avoiding contact with toxic agents, and therefore making this classic reaction safer.

Although the active group is different in these three families, a common reagent could be found allowing the simultaneous determination of all of them, also minimizing the risks involved in handling the mentioned reagent. This reaction, modified by changing both alkylant and catalyser reagents to t-BuOK/DMSO/EtI, gives rise to a simple derivatization method.

The use of chemiometric methods such as ANOVA, Simplex and factorial design show their usefulness for the selection of the alkylant reagents and for optimization of the variables involved in the derivative reactions.

A chromatographic method is available for the simultaneous determination of the three families; carbamates, phenylureas and phenoxy acids, and has been applied to water samples.

In: Materials Science Researcher Biographical Sketches …   ISBN: 978-1-61942-153-0
Editors: Satomi Matsumoto and Ueda Iwate   © 2013 Nova Science Publishers, Inc.

Chapter 120

ADVANCES IN LIQUID CHROMATOGRAPHY FOR THE DETERMINATION OF MYCOTOXINS IN FOODS

R. Romero-González, J. L. Martínez Vidal and A. Garrido Frenich

Research Group "Analytical Chemistry of Contaminants",
Department of Analytical Chemistry, Almeria University, Almeria, Spain

RESEARCH SUMMARY

Despite the intentional use of chemicals, nowadays food contamination due to natural toxicants is also a major public concern. Mycotoxins are secondary metabolites produced by many species of fungi, and they are one of the major contaminants of agricultural products. Because of their high toxicity, many countries have set up regulations for their control in foods of plant origin for humans. In order to fulfill the requirements described in these regulations, sensitive, selective and reliable analytical methods have been developed in order to determine as many mycotoxins as possible in one single analysis.

Traditionally, mycotoxins have been mainly determined by immunoassay screening methods or by single-compound chromatographic analytical methods, based on immuno-affinity column cleanup followed by a separation step using thin layer chromatography (TLC), gas chromatography (GC) or liquid chromatography (LC), which were coupled to conventional detectors such as electron capture detection (ECD), fluorescence or UV-visible detection. In some cases, especially when fluorescence detection was used, it was necessary to include a pre- or post-column derivatization step in order to increase the detection capabilities of the analytical method. However, the application of hyphenated chromatographic techniques, especially LC coupled to mass spectrometry (MS) and LC-MS/MS, has several advantages including simple treatment—since further clean up procedures with immunoaffinity columns can be avoided, rapid determination and high sensitivity. Furthermore, they can be used for the simultaneous determination of several types of mycotoxins in contaminated food samples, although the number of developed methods is still limited.

Despite the determination of regulated mycotoxins, it is important to detect mycotoxins for which standards are not commercially available as well as metabolites produced by fungi involved in food spoilage, and LC coupled to other type of analyzers such as time of flight (TOF), provides valuable information related to these compounds.

An overview of liquid chromatographic methods, providing general aspects regarding the determination of mycotoxins in food and emphasizing the use of hyphenated techniques is presented. Advantages and disadvantages of chromatographic techniques are also evaluated, indicating the new advances which are mainly focused on the reduction of the analysis time. These advances allow the application of the developed methods for the determination of multi-component mycotoxins in routine analysis or in monitoring programs, in which a large number of samples must be analyzed.

In: Materials Science Researcher Biographical Sketches ...   ISBN: 978-1-61942-153-0
Editors: Satomi Matsumoto and Ueda Iwate   © 2013 Nova Science Publishers, Inc.

Chapter 121

HISTORICAL OVERVIEW OF CHROMATOGRAPHY AND RELATED TECHNIQUES IN ANALYSIS OF ANTIMALARIAL DRUG PRIMAQUINE

*Ilia Brondz**

Department of Biology, University of Oslo, Blindern, Oslo, Norway

RESEARCH SUMMARY

Malaria is one of the most widespread and deadly diseases on the planet. It has killed more people than all wars, famines, earthquakes and tsunamis in the course of human history. The construction of the Panama Canal was nearly stopped because of a high death toll from malaria among workers. Today, malaria is a disease not only limited poor areas around world, but it has also returned to Southern European countries such as Italy and France. Every year around 500 million new cases are diagnosed; the death toll is about 3 million people per year. Children are most vulnerable to this disease, and in Africa, childhood deaths from malaria account for about 90% of total human deaths from this disease on that continent.

The primaquine (CAS 90-34-6) is used for causative treatment of malaria. Primaquine has high antiparasitic effects against gametocytes and thus the ability to prevent a spread of the parasite from patients under treatment to mosquitoes. It is also used in radical cures and prevents relapses. Consequently, primaquine is an often-used drug.

Primaquine is synthetic, mostly replicating the natural antimalarial drug quinine.

Primaquine was synthesized for the first time in USA about sixty years ago.

From the first step of synthesis to the production floor the drug is analyzed qualitatively and quantitatively. Today's techniques used in monitoring of quality and quantity of the drug are different types of chromatography. Some classic and instrumental techniques as spectrometry are also used to ensure correct results.

In the presented chapter, the Craig's technique used by Elderfield and colleges during experimentation of the first synthesis of primaquine to cutting edge techniques like gas chromatography – mass spectrometry with a supersonic molecular beam (GC-MS with SMB),

---

* E-mail: ilia.brondz@bio.uio.no ilia.brondz@gmail.com.

which is not yet commercial available, are discussed. Thin-layer chromatography (TLC), high performance chromatography (HPLC) – mass spectrometry (MS), gas chromatography (GC)-mass spectrometry (MS), supercritical fluid chromatography (SFC)- mass spectrometry (MS), capillary electrophoresis (CE) and other analyzing and detecting techniques are described in application to the primaquine analysis. UV, CD, NMR and MS spectrometry, does the verification of authenticity.

A short description of every technique is given together with a comparison of practical advantages and disadvantages of the techniques.

A short scope of related techniques used for analysis of primaquine and analogues follows the technical discussion.

There are several approaches to analyzing the quality and quantity of primaquine in raw ware and medical form as tablets today. New developments in this field are critically reviewed and the general situation on the antimalarial drug marked is presented.

In: Materials Science Researcher Biographical Sketches ...   ISBN: 978-1-61942-153-0
Editors: Satomi Matsumoto and Ueda Iwate   © 2013 Nova Science Publishers, Inc.

Chapter 122

CHROMATOGRAPHY IN THE RESEARCH OF PHENOLIC SECONDARY METABOLITES

Jan Vacek[*1] and Bořivoj Klejdus[2]*

[1]Department of Medical Chemistry and Biochemistry,
Faculty of Medicine and Dentistry, Palacký University Olomouc,
Olomouc, Czech Republic
[2]Department of Chemistry and Biochemistry, Mendel University of Agriculture and
Forestry in Brno, Brno, Czech Republic

RESEARCH SUMMARY

Developments in liquid chromatography separations of bioactive phenolic compounds and their exact identifications in plant samples and phytopharmaceutical products by mass spectrometry methods are described in this chapter. The main aim of the text is to present the application of both modern and the most recent methods, especially high-performance and ultrahigh-pressure liquid chromatography, in the study of phenolic secondary metabolites.

[*] e-mail: jan.vacek@upol.cz.

In: Materials Science Researcher Biographical Sketches ...   ISBN: 978-1-61942-153-0
Editors: Satomi Matsumoto and Ueda Iwate   © 2013 Nova Science Publishers, Inc.

Chapter 123

AUTOMATED ON-LINE COUPLING LIQUID CHROMATOGRAPHY-GAS CHROMATOGRAPHY AND LARGE VOLUME INJECTION BY USING THE TOTAD INTERFACE

Jose Manuel Cortés[1], Rosa María Toledano[1], Juan Carlos Andini[2], Jesús Villén[1] and Ana María Vázquez[3]*

[1]Escuela Técnica Superior de Ingenieros Agrónomos. Departamento de Ciencia y Tecnología Agroforestal y Genética. Universidad de Castilla-La Mancha, Albacete, Spain
[2]CCT-CONICET SANTA FE. Güemes, Santa Fe. Argentina.
[3]Escuela Universitaria de Magisterio de Albacete. Departamento de Química-Física. Universidad de Castilla-La Mancha, Albacete, Spain

RESEARCH SUMMARY

In the chromatographic trace analysis of complex matrices, small sample size, simple sample preparation, good sensitivity and full automation are all highly desirable characteristics. Large volume injection (LVI) and on-line coupled liquid chromatography-gas chromatography (LC-GC) have become powerful tools in an attempt to achieve these goals. LVI increases sensitivity and/or reduces the need for extract concentration steps. In coupled LC-GC, the specific components of a complex matrix are pre-fractionated by LC and then transferred on-line to the highly efficient and sensitive GC system for analytical separation.

The problem with both techniques is basically the same: how to introduce into the GC system a volume of a liquid sample, extract or eluent from LC, far above that usually injected in GC.

In order to achieve this, reliable interfaces, if possible automatic, which allow the solvent to be eliminated and analytes to be retained without loss or contamination, are necessary. For

---
* Corresponding author. Email: jesus.villen@uclm.es.

such a purpose TOTAD (Through Oven Transfer Adsorption Desorption) was designed: this interface allows the LVI of polar and non-polar solvents and, consequently, on-line LC-GC when LC is carried out in normal as well as in reversed phase. The TOTAD interface is based on a thoroughly modified PTV injector, the changes introduced in the same affecting its pneumatics, sample introduction and solvent elimination. An eluent from an LC system can be sent to the interface or to waste by a six port valve. When sent to the GC system, the eluent passes through the liner. This is filled with an adsorbent or absorbent material, which retains the analytes while the eluent is eliminated to waste through a stainless steel tube situated on the external side of the liner, pushed by helium flowing in an opposite direction to the GC column carrier gas flow. The eluent is vented in both evaporative and non-evaporative mode. During the transfer, the interface and oven temperature are kept low and after the transfer, the TOTAD interface is rapidly heated and the retained analytes are thermally desorbed and transferred to the GC column. Main modifications made to the initial interface, previously unpublished, are explained.

Different analytical methods by LVI and RPLC-GC using the TOTAD interface have been developed. LVI with TOTAD interface allows the analysis of pesticides in river water by sampling volumes as large as 1 ml. LVI of vegetables extracts obtained with a small amount of ethyl acetate and anhydrous sodium sulphate allows pesticide residues to be analysed. If pesticide residues have to be analysed in samples of a fatty nature, such as olive oil or nuts, the coupling of RPLC and GC using the TOTAD interface can effectively separates the fatty compounds in the RPLC step. Olive oil simply needs to be filtered before the chromatographic analysis. In the analysis of nuts, pesticides are extracted with a small amount of ethyl acetate and anhydrous sodium sulphate, and the extract is directly injected in the chromatographic system with no need for concentration or clean-up steps. An automated method for the analysis of unsaponifiable compounds in edible oils has also been developed. The method allows the analysis of different groups of compounds (free sterols, tocopherols, squalene and erythrodiol and uvaol) in one chromatographic run or the analysis of these compounds in different groups. A method for analysing methyl-jasmonate in aromatic samples by RPLC-GC has been developed.

All the above methods practically eliminate the time-consuming sample preparation step, present high sensitivity and good repeatability. No variability in the retention time is observed, which can be a problem in other LC-GC coupling systems. Good performance is achieved at different eluent and helium flow rates during the transfer step. TOTAD is a versatile and fully automatic interface highly suitable for LVI and on-line NPLC-GC and RPLC-GC coupling.

In: Materials Science Researcher Biographical Sketches …   ISBN: 978-1-61942-153-0
Editors: Satomi Matsumoto and Ueda Iwate   © 2013 Nova Science Publishers, Inc.

Chapter 124

Coupling Chromatography and Mass Spectrometry for the Study of Organotin Compounds in the Marine Environment

Marina Di Carro and Emanuele Magi[*]

Dipartimento di Chimica e Chimica Industriale, Sezione di Chimica Analitica ed Ambientale, Università di Genova, Genova, Italy

Research Summary

Organotin compounds (OTCs) have been extensively studied in the last decades due to their toxicity and considerable impact on the aquatic environment. The general class of triorganotins are favored as selective biocides: marine paints containing tributyltin (TBT) have been found to be very effective in eliminating fouling problems to all types of ships. These paints usually contain up to 20% of organotin compound which is slowly leached into the water and have an active lifetime of 1-2 years. Butyltins have been shown to interfere with the biological processes of several species, causing disorders in the hormonal system. In the marine environment TBT degrades into more polar compounds, dibutyltin (DBT) and monobutyltin (MBT), less toxic to aquatic organisms.

The International Maritime Organization (IMO) adopted an International Convention for the ban of organotin compounds which partly failed to be transposed into domestic legislation in several countries, including non-EU Mediterranean nations, and TBT-based antifouling paints are still used. Different studies worldwide have shown a slow decline in TBT contamination, although OTCs concentrations are still relevant in several areas.

In order to evaluate the distribution and fate of OTCs in the marine environment, several analytical methods have been developed. The most commonly used analytical techniques employ chromatography (LC and GC) coupled with selective and sensitive detectors: mass spectrometry (MS), atomic emission spectrometry (AES), flame photometry (FPD) and inductively coupled plasma mass spectrometry (ICP-MS).

---

[*] Tel #39.010.3536113/87 fax #39.010.3536190, e-mail: magie@chimica.unige.it.

This work presents a review of the hyphenated methods developed in our laboratory during the last decade for the study of marine matrices. They are discussed and compared with other methods reported in the recent literature, considering the different analytical performances.

Furthermore, the optimization of the sample preparation is discussed taking into account all the steps involved: extraction from the real matrix, derivatization and clean-up.

In: Materials Science Researcher Biographical Sketches ...   ISBN: 978-1-61942-153-0
Editors: Satomi Matsumoto and Ueda Iwate   © 2013 Nova Science Publishers, Inc.

Chapter 125

SOLID-PHASE EXTRACTION AS AN ALTERNATIVE TO THIN-LAYER CHROMATOGRAPHY IN PHYTOSTEROL ANALYSIS

Sodeif Azadmard-Damirchi[*]

Department of Food Science and Technology, Faculty of Agriculture,
University of Tabriz, Tabriz, Iran

RESEARCH SUMMARY

Suitable preparative methods in the analysis of phytosterols help to obtain accurate results. Thin-layer chromatography (TLC) is a conventional preparative method in analysis of phytosterols, but this method has some drawbacks. Solid-phase extraction (SPE) is a simple and inexpensive chromatographic method. SPE has been widely used in the preparation of lipid classes such as phytosterols prior to further analyses by GC and GC-MS. Phytosterols comprise a major proportion of the unsaponifiables in vegetable oils. They are divided into three main classes: 4-desmethylsterols, 4-monomethylsterols, and 4,4'-dimethylsterols. Methylsterols usually occur in relatively low amount and therefore it is necessary to separate and enrich them by preparative chromatographic methods before quantification by GC. Phytosterols also occur either in free form or esterified with fatty acids and other conjugates. Separation of free and esterified phytosterols by preparative methods before quantification by GC provides detailed information on their distribution and stability. Phytosterols can also oxidize in the same way as other unsaturated lipids and produce phytosterol oxidation products (POPs) which may have possible toxicity effects at higher concentrations. Separation and enrichment of POPs from bulk lipids is an essential step before quantification and identification by GC or GC–MS. In this chapter, TLC methods and their drawbacks in the preparation of phytosterols before analysis by GC and GC-MS and advantage of SPE method as an alternative method to conventional TLC methods, is discussed.

---

[*] Phone: + 98-411 3392032. Fax: + 98- 411 3345332, E-mail: s-azadmard@tabrizu.ac.ir.

In: Materials Science Researcher Biographical Sketches ...   ISBN: 978-1-61942-153-0
Editors: Satomi Matsumoto and Ueda Iwate   © 2013 Nova Science Publishers, Inc.

Chapter 126

ANALYSIS OF PROPYLENE GLYCOL IN AIRPORT SURFACE RUNOFF BY SOLID-PHASE MICRO EXTRACTION (SPME) AND GAS CHROMATOGRAPHY/MASS SPECTROMETRY (GC/MS)

Elke Fries and Sven Ernesti*
University of Osnabrück, Osnabrück, Germany

RESEARCH SUMMARY

Different mixtures of propylene glycol (PG) and water are widely used for aircraft de-icing and anti-icing operations in wintry weather conditions. Although waste water that is highly contaminated with aircraft de-icing and anti-icing fluids (ADAF) is collected after application and disposed adequately in waste water treatment plants, a diffuse input of PG into the environment must be regarded. Main input sources are wind drift during application, runoff from aircraft surfaces until it arrives at take-off position, and removal of ADAF from aircraft surfaces during takeoff.

In this article, the analysis of PG in aqueous solutions by solid-phase microextraction (SPME) and gas chromatography (GC) combined with mass spectrometry (MS) is presented. PG is a very polar compound with a great affinity to water. Thus, an efficient extraction of PG from water is of high priority to reach a low limit of detection (LOD). PG was directly extracted by the SPME fiber from water samples of low sample volume (18 ml). Two SPME fibers, an 85-µm Polydimethylsiloxane (PDMS)/Carboxen fiber and an 85-µm Polyacrylate (PA) fiber were evaluated for extraction efficiency. Higher amounts of PG were extracted from the water using the 85µm-PDMS/Carboxen fiber. Optimum SPME conditions for this fiber were obtained using an extraction temperature of 60 °C, an extraction time of 30 minutes, a fiber desorption time of 13 minutes at 250 °C and a fiber bake-out time of 20

---

* Corresponding author. Tel.: +49 541 969 3441; fax: +49 541 969 2599, E-mail address: fries@usf.uos.de (E. Fries)

minutes at 310 °C. Based on these conditions the LOD was 0.115 mg L^{-1}. The limit of quantification (LOQ) was set at three times the LOD and was 0.345 mg L^{-1}. The LOD of the SPME/GC-MS method was at least one order of magnitude better than those of common analytical methods based on liquid-liquid extraction of PG from the water phase. Using $[^2H]_4$-ethylene glycol (ethylene glycol-d4) as an internal standard the relative standard deviation (RSD) at a PG concentration of 0.504 mg L^{-1} was 14.6 % demonstrating a good reproducibility of the method at a concentration nearby the LOQ. The SPME/GC-MS method was applied successfully to analyze PG in airport surface run-off with a mean concentration of 10.75 mg/l (n=3) demonstrating a diffuse input of PG from aircraft de-icing and anti-icing operations.

In: Materials Science Researcher Biographical Sketches ...   ISBN: 978-1-61942-153-0
Editors: Satomi Matsumoto and Ueda Iwate   © 2013 Nova Science Publishers, Inc.

Chapter 127

IDENTIFICATION OF VOLATILE COMPOUNDS IN MAPLE SYRUP USING HEADSPACE SOLID-PHASE MICROEXTRACTION WITH GAS CHROMATOGRAPHY-MASS SPECTROMETRY

Hassan Sabik[*,1]*, Jacinthe Fortin*[1] *and Nathalie Martin*[2]

[1]Food Research and Development Centre, Agriculture and Agri-Food Canada,
St-Hyacinthe, Quebec, Canada
[2]Centre de recherche, de développement et de transfert technologique acéricole inc.
(Centre ACER), St-Hyacinthe, Quebec, Canada

RESEARCH SUMMARY

Headspace solid-phase microextraction (HS-SPME) combined with gas chromatography-mass spectrometry (GC/MS) was applied to identify volatile compounds in four typical maple syrups. Carboxen/polydimethylsiloxane (CAR/PDMS, 85 µm) fibre was selected as the fibre of choice because of its high capacity to extract both volatile and semi-volatile compounds. The following conditions were selected for HS-SPME analysis: 1) extraction temperature of 40°C and extraction time of 44 min for volatile compounds; and 2) extraction temperature of 67°C and extraction time of 60 min for semi-volatile compounds. A 1-g portion of maple syrup, diluted with 1 mL of NaCl solution (6 M), was sufficient to get the desired sensitivity. A total of 204 volatile compounds were identified by comparing their mass spectra and retention times with injected standards and/or by searching the Mass Spectral Library database of the National Institute of Standards and Technology. Of those compounds, 63 were found to be food aromatic compounds belonging to the following chemical families: acids (1), alcohols (3), aldehydes (8), aromatic compounds (2), esters (1), furan derivatives (15), hydrocarbons (3), ketones (10), pyrazines (15) and miscellaneous substances (5). To our knowledge, 50 of those aromatic compounds had not previously been detected in maple syrup.

---

[*] Fax: 1-450-773-8461, E-mail: hassan.sabik@agr.gc.ca.

In: Materials Science Researcher Biographical Sketches …   ISBN: 978-1-61942-153-0
Editors: Satomi Matsumoto and Ueda Iwate   © 2013 Nova Science Publishers, Inc.

Chapter 128

DETERMINATION OF NICOTINE AND COTININE IN HUMAN URINE WITH MEMBRANE ASSISTED THREE PHASE MICROEXTRACTION AND AQUEOUS REVERSED-PHASE LIQUID CHROMATOGRAPHY

Ming-Ren Fuh*, Li-Lung Chen, Mahaveer B. Melwanki and Shu-Ling Lin

Department of Chemistry, Soochow University, Taipei, Taiwan

RESEARCH SUMMARY

Three phase microextraction with the automated movement of the acceptor and the donor phase (TPME/AMADP) technique is described for the extraction of nicotine (NT) and cotinine (CT) from non-smokers' urine. Separation and quantitative analyses were performed using aqueous reversed-phase liquid chromatography (LC) equipped with ultra-violet (UV) detector. The target compounds were extracted from a basified sample solution (donor phase) into a few microliters of the organic solvent impregnated in the pores of the hollow fiber and then back extracted into an acidic solution (acceptor phase) inside the lumen of the hollow fiber. The fiber was held by a conventional 10 µl LC syringe. Five microliter acidic aqueous acceptor phase was sand-witched between the plunger and another 2 µl of an organic solvent (microcap). The microcap separated the acceptor phase and the donor phase; in addition, it was partially responsible for mass transfer of the analytes from the donor solution to the acceptor solution. The acceptor solution was repeatedly moved in and out of the hollow fiber using a syringe pump. This movement provided a fresh acceptor phase to come in contact with the organic phase and improved in enrichment of the analytes. Additionally, fresh donor phase entered through the open end of the hollow fiber also contributed to the mass transfer. Various parameters affecting the extraction efficiency, *viz,* type of organic solvent, extraction time, stirring speed, effect of sodium chloride, and concentration of donor and acceptor

---

* Corresponding author. Tel: +886-2-28819471 ext. 6821; Fax: +886-2-28811053, Email address: msfuh@mail.scu.edu.tw (M. -R. Fuh).

phases were studied. Precision (RSD=3.23 and 3.51% respectively for nicotine and cotinine: tested at three concentration levels), linearity (correlation coefficient, r^2=0.9964 and 0.9985 respectively for nicotine and cotinine), detection limit (9.7 and 194.5 ng/ml respectively for nicotine and cotinine), enrichment factor (158 and 6 respectively for nicotine and cotinine), relative recovery (83 and 85% respectively for nicotine and cotinine) and absolute recovery (9.6 and 12.0 % respectively for nicotine and cotinine) have also been obtained. The developed method was applied for the analysis of non-smokers' urine.

In: Materials Science Researcher Biographical Sketches …   ISBN: 978-1-61942-153-0
Editors: Satomi Matsumoto and Ueda Iwate   © 2013 Nova Science Publishers, Inc.

Chapter 129

π-π ACTIVE STATIONARY PHASES IMMOBILIZED WITH ORGANIC DYES OR ITS ANALOGUES FOR HIGH-PERFORMANCE LIQUID CHROMATOGRAPHY AND CAPILLARY ELECTROCHROMATOGRAPHY

Kaname Ohyama[1], Kenichiro Nakashima[2], Mitsuhiro Wada[2], Naoya Kishikawa[1] and Naotaka Kuroda[1]

[1]Department of Environmental and Pharmaceutical Sciences, Graduate School of Biomedical Sciences, Nagasaki University
[2]Department of Clinical Pharmacy, Graduate School of Biomedical Sciences, Nagasaki University, Japan

RESEARCH SUMMARY

High-performance liquid chromatography (HPLC) is a widely accepted technique for the biological, environmental and food analyses. Capillary electrochromatography (CEC), which is a hybrid of capillary electrophoresis and HPLC, is one of the most rapidly developing techniques for separation analysis. The separation of analytes in both chromatographic methods is achieved by a stationary phase; therefore, much effort has been devoted to the design of stationary phases. Octadecyl silica (ODS) is currently the most popular and widely applied stationary phase in HPLC and CEC. In parallel, recent trends have been directed toward the development of new packing materials having selectivity in the recognition of biologically important substances. For this purpose, the stationary phases with π-electron are proved to be promising because of its unique retention behavior provided by π-π interaction. These stationary phases are advantageous for the case that good separation cannot be obtained on ODS and some of them often give good results in chiral separation. Actually, several types of column packed with those stationary phases have been reported as a laboratory-made or are available as a commercial product.

* Tel.: +81-95-819-2894; fax: +81-95-819-2444. E-mail address: n-kuro@nagasaki-u.ac.jp.

Here, we introduce (*N*-substituted)aminopropyl-modified silica gels with π-π active aromatic moieties which were successfully utilized in HPLC and CEC.

In: Materials Science Researcher Biographical Sketches ...   ISBN: 978-1-61942-153-0
Editors: Satomi Matsumoto and Ueda Iwate   © 2013 Nova Science Publishers, Inc.

Chapter 130

DETERMINATION OF WATER-SOLUBLE TOXINS AND PHARMACEUTICALS IN BIOLOGICAL MATERIALS USING HYDROPHILIC INTERACTION LIQUID CHROMATOGRAPHY

Akihiro Nakamoto[1], Manami Nishida[2], Takeshi Saito[3] and Akira Namera[*,4]*

[1]Scientific Investigation Laboratory, Hiroshima Prefectural Police Headquarters, Kohnan, Naka-ku, Hiroshima, Japan
[2]Hiroshima University Technical Center, Kaumi, Minami-ku, Hiroshima, Japan
[3]Department of Emergency and Critical Care Medicine, Tokai University School of Medicine, Isehara, Kanagawa, Japan
[4]Department of Forensic Medicine, Graduate School of Biomedical Sciences, Hiroshima University, Minami-ku, Hiroshima, Japan

RESEARCH SUMMARY

Normal phase liquid chromatography (NPLC) has been widely used for the separation of polar compounds. In NPLC, a non-aqueous organic solution is used as the mobile phase. It is difficult to separate polar compounds in the mobile phase. Therefore, NPLC finds limited application in the separation of polar compounds from biological materials. Polar compounds are poorly retained in a reversed phase (RP) column, even if a highly aqueous mobile phase is used. For RPLC–mass spectrometry with electrospray ionization, poor analyte on-column retention may result in detrimental matrix effects and high water content. The mobile phase is also not conducive to achieving good spray conditions.

Hydrophilic interaction LC (HILIC) is a relatively new separation technique used for polar and water-soluble compounds. HILIC with bare silica as the stationary phase and a low-

---

[*] E-mail: namera@hiroshima-u.ac.jp.

aqueous/high-organic solution as the mobile phase has been used for the determination of polar compounds in biological materials. Neutral and hydrophobic endogenous interferences present in biological materials will not be retained on the column.

Marine toxins and pharmaceuticals such as tetrodotoxin, saxitoxin, and antibiotics give rise to many polar compounds that act as contaminants. So far, RPLC and/or ion-pairing chromatography have been examined in order to separate and identify polar compounds in biological materials; however, some problems remain unsolved. The high-aqueous mobile phase or ion-paring reagents were ionized in the mass spectrometer. To overcome this problem, we have investigated the use of HILIC for separating polar compounds by using a low-aqueous/high-organic mobile phase. This article summarizes applications to separate marine toxins and pharmaceuticals that cause poisoning. We also describe HILIC's potential to determine toxins and pharmaceuticals in biological materials.

In: Materials Science Researcher Biographical Sketches ...   ISBN: 978-1-61942-153-0
Editors: Satomi Matsumoto and Ueda Iwate   © 2013 Nova Science Publishers, Inc.

Chapter 131

RECENTLY DEVELOPED TECHNIQUES FOR EXTRACTION OF DRUGS AND MEDICINES DURING CHROMATOGRAPHIC DETERMINATION IN TOXICOLOGICAL ANALYSIS

Akira Namera[*,1], *Akihiro Nakamoto*[2], *Takeshi Saito*[3] *and Manami Nishida*[4]

[1]Hiroshima University, Hiroshima, Japan
[2]Hiroshima Prefectural Police Headquarters, Hiroshima, Japan
[3]Tokai University School of Medicine, Kanagawa, Japan
[4]Hiroshima University Technical Center, Hiroshima, Japan

RESEARCH SUMMARY

Some problems have been encountered in the chromatographic determination of drugs and pharmaceuticals in biological materials, such as low concentration of analytes, a complicated matrix, and the limited sample volume available for analysis. Overcoming these problems is one of the most challenging tasks in toxicological analysis. Endogenous interferences must be removed, and the analytes must be concentrated prior to chromatographic determination. These problems cannot be overcome even by improving the performance of analytical equipment. In clinical, toxicological, and environmental analyses, the process involving purification, concentration, and derivatization of analytes is called "sample preparation." Liquid-liquid extraction (LLE) has been widely used for sample preparation because of its usefulness and low cost of operation. In the LLE technique, analytes are systematically extracted and purified by using the chemical characteristics of the analytes. However, a large amount of extraction solvent is required, and the extraction process is complicated. Moreover, the organic solvents used in this technique are toxic to both humans and the environment. The procedure is also time-consuming, and the number of samples that can be simultaneously treated is limited. The formation of emulsion during

---

[*] Author to whom correspondence should be addressed: E-mail, namera@hiroshima-u.ac.jp.

extraction is also a critical problem. To overcome these problems, solid-phase extraction (SPE) was developed. In the SPE technique, silica gel or polymer resins are embedded in a cartridge as a solid adsorbed material. The analytes are adsorbed onto the surface of the sorbent when the sample solution flows through the cartridge. Endogenous interferences can be removed by passing an aqueous solution through the cartridge. Sorbent materials can be selected according to the behavior of the analytes. The LLE and SPE methods involve laborious, intensive, and expensive preparatory procedures. Moreover, in both these methods, the eluated solution finally has to be removed by evaporation.

To avoid these complicated and time-consuming steps, new techniques have been recently developed to reduce the size of the previously used devices or inject all the adsorbed analytes into the analytical equipment. In this chapter, some unique and useful techniques and devices for the chromatographic determination of drugs and pharmaceuticals in biological materials are introduced.

In: Materials Science Researcher Biographical Sketches ...   ISBN: 978-1-61942-153-0
Editors: Satomi Matsumoto and Ueda Iwate   © 2013 Nova Science Publishers, Inc.

Chapter 132

USE OF EVAPORATIVE LIGHT SCATTERING DETECTION (ELSD) FOR THE QUALITY CONTROL OF DRUG SUBSTANCES

Ulrike Holzgrabe[*,1], *Daniela Brinz*[1], *Christine Weber*[1] *and Stefan Almeling*[2]

[1]University of Würzburg, Würzburg, Germany
[2]European Directorate for the Quality of Medicines and Health Care, Strasbourg, France

RESEARCH SUMMARY

HPLC with evaporative light scattering detection (ELSD) is a versatile, easy to use and inexpensive alternative when it comes to the analysis of substances lacking of a chromophore for UV detection. This is particularly true when the amounts of the analytes to be determined are not too different from one another, as is the case e. g. for drugs such as gentamicin which is composed of five closely related components of 2 to 40 percent. The same applies to the characterization of polymers, such as polyethylene glycols (PEGs). However, in HPLC analysis for quality control of drugs with a content greater than 95 % injections of highly concentrated test solutions are normally required to control impurities at low levels between 0.05 and 0.5 percent. Under these conditions spike peaks can appear on the tail of the main peak making a proper evaluation of the impurity profile impossible. The influence of different LC and ELSD parameters like eluent flow rate, ELSD scavenger gas flow rate, evaporation temperature and mobile phase composition on the appearance of spike peaks will be discussed in addition to the impact of these parameters on the method sensitivity. The results obtained from the ELSD will be compared to findings with the charged aerosol detection (CAD).

[*] Corresponding author:Prof. Dr. Ulrike Holzgrabe, University of Würzburg, Institute for pharmacy and food chemistry, Am Hubland, 97074 Würzburg, Germany, Phone: +49-931-31-85461; Fax +49-931-888-5494, Email: u.holzgrabe@pharmazie.uni-wuerzburg.de.

In: Materials Science Researcher Biographical Sketches …   ISBN: 978-1-61942-153-0
Editors: Satomi Matsumoto and Ueda Iwate   © 2013 Nova Science Publishers, Inc.

Chapter 133

HIGH-THROUGHPUT CHROMAGRAPHIC IN MYCOTOXIN AND PHYCOTOXIN ANALYSIS: CUTTING EDGE APPLICATIONS WITH FOCUS ON THE DETERMINATION OF AMNESIC SHELLFISH POISONING TOXINS IN SHELLFISH

Pablo de la Iglesia[*,1,2], *Gemma Giménez*[1,2],
María Luisa Rodríguez-Velasco[3], *Adriano Villar-González*[3]
and Jorge Diogène[1,2]

[1]Institut de Recerca i Tecnologia Agroalimentàries (IRTA),
Sant Carles de la Ràpita, Tarragona, Spain
[2]XRAq. Xarxa de Referència en Aqüicultura. Generalitat de Catalunya
[3]Community Reference Laboratory for Marine Biotoxins (CRLMB).
Agencia Española de Seguridad Alimentaria y Nutrición (AESAN),
Estación Marítima S/N. Muelle de Trasatlánticos, Vigo, Spain

RESEARCH SUMMARY

The application of fast chromatography methods aimed at reducing the analysis time is still highly demanded by research and routine laboratories. A short analysis time allows decreasing the period spent on method development and validations, providing a fast reply against emerging hazards. In addition, routine applications can also be favored by improving the response of surveillance programs against sudden food safety alerts. Even more, the lower operation cost and solvent consumption usually related to fast chromatography are causing rapid resolution methods to gain momentum in the field of food analysis.

This chapter includes, in the first part, a review of the cutting edge applications of rapid chromatography for the determination of mycotoxins and phycotoxins, which are natural toxins produced by fungi and algae, respectively, with an impact on food safety and public

---

* Contact author: Phone.: +34 977 745 427; Fax: +34 977 744 138; e-mail: pablo.delaiglesia@irta.cat.

health. In the second part, we present our contribution with the application of rapid resolution liquid chromatography on a 1.8 µm-particle packed column coupled with tandem mass spectrometry (RRLC-MS/MS) for the analysis of amnesic shellfish poisoning (ASP) toxins in shellfish. The main parameters affecting the chromatographic performance in columns packed with sub-2µm particle size are discussed for the analysis of ASP toxins. The application to shellfish extracts allowed the complete resolution among domoic acid and the isomers A, D and epidomoic acid in less than 3 minutes. The preliminary evaluation of the method has shown high sensitivity with a limit of detection of 0.03 ng mL^{-1} corresponding to 0.2 10^{-3} mg kg^{-1} of shellfish tissue, and linearity in the range of 1–100 ng mL^{-1} (0.006–0.667 mg kg^{-1}) with a coefficient r^2 = 0.9999, although with the presence of some matrix effects for the analysis of crude shellfish extracts in methanol:water (1:1). The comparison between RRLC-MS/MS and the reference LC-UV method (n=86) has resulted in a lineal regression with a slope of 1.0711, intercept of 0.013 and r^2 = 0.997. These results, together with that obtained in the inter-laboratory exercise organized by the Community Reference Laboratory on Marine Biotoxins (CRLMB) during 2008 for ASP toxins analysis (z-score = 0.093) allow us to conclude that for these toxins, rapid resolution liquid chromatography provided additional advantages while the performance and reliability of the results were maintained. Additional improvements related with sample extraction are also explored to increase the sample throughput.

In: Materials Science Researcher Biographical Sketches ...   ISBN: 978-1-61942-153-0
Editors: Satomi Matsumoto and Ueda Iwate   © 2013 Nova Science Publishers, Inc.

Chapter 134

RECENT TRENDS IN SAMPLE PREPARATION AND ANALYSIS

M. A. Rostagno[*]

Centro para la Calidad de los Alimentos, Instituto Nacional de Investigación y
Tecnología Agraria y Alimentaria (INIA), Campus Universitario
"Duques de Soria", Soria, Soria, Spain

The appearance of robust and reliable hyphenated systems, such as LC-MS and GC-MS, for the detection, quantification and/or identification of compounds, represents one of the most important recent developments in analytical science. Additional spectroscopic and spectrometric techniques (e.g., UV, DAD, IR, NMR, etc.) may also be coupled onto these systems providing yet higher performance and multi-parameter detection and analysis systems.

Nevertheless, there is a never ending continuous need for faster, more efficient systems for performing higher-quality sample analysis and information gathering. The development of real fully automated analytical methods, where the whole process is completed without intervention (including sampling, sample preparation and dissolution, interference removal, aliquot withdrawal, analyte measurement, data processing, result evaluation and decision making), is the one of the major future goals in modern analytical chemistry.

Integration of sample preparation techniques to hyphenated analysis systems is a natural necessity for the development of fully automated analytical methods. In this context, modern extraction techniques such as microwave-assisted extraction (MAE), ultrasound-assisted extraction (UAE), pressurized liquid extraction (PLE), supercritical fluid extraction (SFE) or solid-phase extraction (SPE) are an attractive choice to be integrated in hyphenated systems since they are fast, highly efficient, consume low amount of solvents and sample and more importantly, have a high degree of automation and be easily coupled online with the analysis technique. Integration of sample preparation to hyphenated analysis systems can drastically reduce the overall time required in a given analytical method, increasing sample throughput and significantly reducing variability derived from sample manipulation.

---

[*] Corresponding author e-mail: rostagno.mauricio@inia.es, Telephone: (+34) 975 233204, Fax: (+34) 975 233205.

During the last decade there has been an impressive increase of the use of modern sample preparation techniques coupled with different analytical techniques. Coupling of MAE, UAE, PLE, SFE and SPE with LC or with GC (both with and without mass spectrometry) and different detectors are nowadays relatively common and several different applications for a wide range of analytes and matrices can be found in the literature.

However, hyphenated systems are still evolving and are now being taken to a new level of complexity and diversity by multiple on-line coupling of different analysis and detection techniques and multidimensional approaches (such as LC-GC-IR(NMR), GC-IR(NMR)-MS, SFC-GC-MS, SFC-GC-IR (NMR), LC-LC-MS, GC-GC-MS, LC-NMR-MS, which is also called "hypernation".

Sample preparation is following in the same direction and combination of different sample preparation techniques in one single step is one of the most recent trends in analytical chemistry. There are already some reports of hyphenated sample preparation, such as UAE-PLE, UAE-SFE, UAE-SPE and SFE-SPE. Furthermore, not only extraction but several different sample preparation procedures can be performed simultaneously or on-line with the analytical system, such as filtration, reactions (i.e. oxidation, hydrolysis, derivatization), and sample clean-up and purification. The combination of several procedures in one single step reduces sample handling and can significantly minimize processing time and the overall duration for the determination of a certain target analyte.

From the evidence available, it is feasible to assume and to hypothesize that these combinatory techniques will converge into a more powerful hypernated technique(s), combining sample preparation and analysis, which will be capable of a full comprehensive multicomponent analysis in a single step of the most complex matrixes, providing huge amounts of information in a timely and user-friendly fashion while at the same time achieving remarkable high performance in terms of speed, limits of detection, reproducibility, accuracy and precision.

In: Materials Science Researcher Biographical Sketches ...   ISBN: 978-1-61942-153-0
Editors: Satomi Matsumoto and Ueda Iwate   © 2013 Nova Science Publishers, Inc.

Chapter 135

POST –IMPACT-FATIGUE BEHAVIOUR OF COMPOSITE LAMINATES: CURRENT AND NOVEL TECHNOLOGIES FOR ENHANCED DAMAGE TOLERANCE

Alkis Paipetis[1] and Dionysios T. G. Katerelos[2]
[1]Department of Materials Science & Engineering,
University of Ioannina, Ioannina, Greece
[2]Department of Sound & Musical Instruments Technology, Technological Educational
Institute of Ionian Islands, Lixouri, Greece

RESEARCH SUMMARY

During their service life, composite laminates are subjected to various transient loadings which often lead to the deterioration of their structural integrity. This deterioration may be manifested in various forms; with increasing impact energy these forms range from delamination to flexural damage to penetration. Among the aforementioned damage modes, delamination is of primary importance as (i) it is invisible and consequently requires non destructive evaluation and (ii) it comprises a considerable damage volume in the affected composite laminate compared to other impact induced damage. The residual properties of laminates deteriorate largely for energies just sufficient to cause penetration; at higher energies, the penetrating impactor passes through the laminate cleanly causing minimum damage away from the penetration area. Furthermore, the impact induced damage is prone to further propagation as the composite is subjected to cyclic loading during its service life. As the propagation of delamination damage is of critical importance for the structural integrity of the composite, it is imperative to predict the delamination growth once present and, at the same time, to develop technologies that minimize the damage initiation and propagation. The scope of this chapter is to present a thorough overview of the aspects related to post impact damage in composite laminates and its subsequent development under fatigue loading. An introduction on the performance of impacted composite laminates and their constituent phases under cyclic loading will be presented, including special loading cases such as environmental or impact-fatigue. Theoretical semi empirical and numerical models that relate delamination propagation to fatigue loading are also thoroughly reviewed. Then, an overview of the existing technologies that minimize impact damage such as stitching or interleaving will be presented and critically evaluated. Special focus is given in non destructive technologies to detect damage and its propagation. The state of the art technologies to minimise impact damage are presented together with the novel concept of hybrid composite systems that employ nano scale phases in order to enhance specific energy absorption and minimize damage propagation. Finally, the applications of damage tolerance technologies in composite structures are discussed.

In: Materials Science Researcher Biographical Sketches ...   ISBN: 978-1-61942-153-0
Editors: Satomi Matsumoto and Ueda Iwate   © 2013 Nova Science Publishers, Inc.

Chapter 136

COMPOSITE MULTILAYER COATINGS FOR IMPROVED BARRIER PROPERTIES OF PACKAGING BOARD

Caisa Andersson

Karlstad University, Faculty of Technology and Science,
Department of Chemical Engineering, Karlstad, Sweden

RESEARCH SUMMARY

Replacement of petroleum-based plastic films with more environmentally friendly, water-based coatings that provide sufficient barrier protection to paper or paperboard is a major future challenge for the packaging industry. Natural polymers, such as starch or cellulose polysaccharides, exert many interesting properties for packaging applications besides originating from renewable sources. They are abundant in nature and can be extracted and processed at a reasonable cost. They also provide good film forming barrier properties for oxygen and grease. However, the moisture sensitivity of biobased polymers makes them inappropriate as protective films for use in food packaging. This chapter aims to present new research in the field of composite barrier coatings by incorporation of reinforcing fillers to enhance the moisture barrier properties.

Synthetic as well as biobased polymer coatings have been investigated. Composite polymer-filler formulations were prepared by blending nanosized clay in polymer dispersions. A composite material was also prepared by blending synthetic polyester into a biobased polymer dispersion. The composite formulations were applied on top of a three-ply packaging board to form various single- and multilayer laminates. Barrier properties with respect to water vapour permeability, oxygen permeability and water absorption are qualitatively discussed. Both commercial talc-filled barrier dispersion coatings and plastic packaging films were used as references. The properties of single layer and combinations of layers in terms of adhesive properties and synergistic effects were studied by investigation of the surface properties.

This chapter shows that a biopolymer based coating can be reinforced with nanosized clay to give barrier properties competitive to commercial, synthetic coating formulations. A dramatic improvement in barrier properties upon application of a thin top nanocomposite coating on various pre-coated structures could also be observed.

In: Materials Science Researcher Biographical Sketches ...   ISBN: 978-1-61942-153-0
Editors: Satomi Matsumoto and Ueda Iwate   © 2013 Nova Science Publishers, Inc.

Chapter 137

SIMULATION OF ULTIMATE STRENGTH OF FIBER-REINFORCED COMPOSITES BY MEANS OF BRIDGING MICROMECHANICS MODEL

Zheng-Ming Huang[*] and Ye-Xin Zhou[†]
Aerospace Engineering & Applied Mechanics,
Tongji University, Shanghai, P. R. China

RESEARCH SUMMARY

Bridging model is a well-developed micromechanical theory, which can be used to predict mechanical behaviors particularly strengths of laminated composites based on the properties of constituent fiber and resin materials. Internal stresses generated in the fibers and resin of a laminate are explicitly correlated with externally applied stresses on the laminate. Thermal residual stresses due to un-match between thermal expansion coefficients of the fibers and the resin are obtained rigorously. In this chapter, the bridging model development incorporated with updated theory is presented. Computer routine together with input data examples for the First Would Wide Failure Exercise (WWFE–I) problems is given in the appendixes of the chapter.

---

[*] E-mail address: huangzm@mail.tongji.edu.cn. Tel.: (+86)021-65985373.
[†] E-mail address: Caihui6871@163.com. Tel.: (+86)021-65980282.

In: Materials Science Researcher Biographical Sketches ...   ISBN: 978-1-61942-153-0
Editors: Satomi Matsumoto and Ueda Iwate   © 2013 Nova Science Publishers, Inc.

Chapter 138

MICROMECHANICAL ANALYSIS FOR LAMINATED COMPOSITE MATERIALS

B. R. Kim and *H. K. Lee*[†]

Department of Civil and Environmental Engineering,
Korea Advanced Institute of Science and Technology (KAIST)
Yuseong-gu, Daejeon, South Korea

RESEARCH SUMMARY

Laminated composite materials are stacked with unidirectional layers at various orientations of the fiber directions to obtain the desired stiffness and strength properties required an acceptable design (Herakovich, 1998). The synergism between constituents of laminated composite materials gives the superior material properties (e.g., low weight, high stiffness, and high strength) unavailable from the individual constituent (Herakovich, 1998; Walker and Smith, 2003; Wimmer et al., 2006). With rapid growth of the use of laminated composite materials, the need for the performance prediction and estimation of these materials has been increased. The physical properties of the laminated composite materials are generally not isotropic in nature, but rather are typically orthotropic or anisotropic in which the material properties are dependent on the reinforced fibers and material used in the laminated composites, type of the layer, orientation of fiber axis to the applied forces, etc. (Herakovich, 1998; Kaw, 1997). The micromechanical analysis has been extensively used to solve the problems on a finer scale and to relate the mechanics of materials to their microstructure which cannot directly solve by using the traditional continuum analysis based on the continuity, isotropy and homogeneity of materials (Lee and Simunovic, 2000, 2001). This micromechanical analysis for laminated composite materials is reviewed in this chapter.

---

[*] E-mail address: bong-ida@kaist.ac.kr.
[†] E-mail address: leeh@kaist.ac.kr. (Corresponding author.)

In: Materials Science Researcher Biographical Sketches …   ISBN: 978-1-61942-153-0
Editors: Satomi Matsumoto and Ueda Iwate   © 2013 Nova Science Publishers, Inc.

Chapter 139

SMART STRUCTURES FOR WIRELESS COMMUNICATIONS

Seong-Ho Son[1] and Woongbong Hwang[2,]*

[1]Radio Technology Research Department, Electronics and Telecommunications Research Institute (ETRI), Daejeon, Republic of Korea
[2]Department of Mechanical Engineering, Pohang University of Science and Technology (POSTECH), Pohang, Republic of Korea

RESEARCH SUMMARY

Traditional practice in antenna design for wireless communications has been to design the mechanical structure and antenna as separate entities. Thus, most of the conventional antennas are attached to the surface of a structure, which causes structural instability. The structural stability and light-weight aspect are essential demands on load-carrying structures such as a vehicular body. Recently there has been interest in designing a structurally integrated antenna, the so-called *smart-skin antenna*. The smart structure is a composite sandwich structure into which microstrip antennas are embedded for radiating electromagnetic waves. The microstrip antenna is very compatible to the sandwich structure. However, it is important to satisfy both structural and electrical requirements that often conflict. This chapter covers the design concept, material selection, fabrication, mechanical characteristics (bending, buckling, fatigue, and impact), and antenna performance (reflection coefficient, radiation pattern, and antenna gain). Furthermore, several experimental models using the smart-skin antenna technology are presented, from single element antenna to phased-array antenna.

---

* E-mail address: whwang@postech.ac.kr.

In: Materials Science Researcher Biographical Sketches ...   ISBN: 978-1-61942-153-0
Editors: Satomi Matsumoto and Ueda Iwate   © 2013 Nova Science Publishers, Inc.

Chapter 140

COMPARISON BETWEEN LOW VELOCITY IMPACT AND QUASI-STATIC INDENTATION TESTS ON CFRP COMPOSITE LAMINATES

Daniele Ghelli and Giangiacomo Minak[*]
Department of Mechanical Engineering (DIEM)
Alma Mater Studiorum, Università di Bologna, Bologna, Italy

RESEARCH SUMMARY

According to several studies, the damage produced in laminated composites during quasi-static indentation tests may be considered similar to the damage caused by foreign object impact. In order to verify this similarity rigorously, low velocity impact and quasi-static indentation tests were done on quasi-isotropic carbon fibre-epoxy resin matrix laminated plates; the elastic behaviour and material damage induced in the two cases were compared. Both dynamic and quasi-static tests were simulated by a two-dimensional finite element model including geometrical nonlinearity. The examination of failures by visual inspection and by optical and scanning electron microscope showed qualitatively similar damage types in impacted and indented specimens: surface indentation, back-face splitting, delamination, fibre fracture and fibre kinking. On the other hand, energy considerations, together with load-displacement relationship and numerical analysis, indicated that in impacted specimens damage is somewhat more severe, thus limiting the validity of the analogy between low velocity impact and quasi-static indentation.

[*] E-mail address: giangiacomo.minak@unibo.it. Tel. +39 51 2093266, Fax +39 51 2093412. (Corresponding author).

In: Materials Science Researcher Biographical Sketches ...   ISBN: 978-1-61942-153-0
Editors: Satomi Matsumoto and Ueda Iwate   © 2013 Nova Science Publishers, Inc.

Chapter 141

Micro-Nano Engineered Composites: New Directions in Biosensing Technologies

Maria Marti Villalba and James Davis†*

Chemistry, School of Science and Technology, Nottingham Trent University,
Nottingham, UK

RESEARCH SUMMARY

The detection of biological molecules has always been of great interest but the complexity of many biofluids and the possible interference of other matrix components can often make the detection of the target analyte difficult. The resolution capabilities inherent to chromatographic techniques has lead to the latter dominating much of the analytical research effort in recent years. There has, however, been an increasing interest in the development of decentralised testing whereby direct measurement and reporting of the analyte concentration is achieved at the site of the analysis – whether it be in the home, in the workplace or in the field. Electrochemical technologies have found a niche application in such technologies given their inherent suitability towards miniaturisation but their selectivity has always been open to question – particularly when compared with the more established laboratory based procedures. Composite systems based on the complex interplay of biological and synthetic recognition components with modern materials has led to a revolution in the applicability of such hybrid devices and has effectively opened up a new vista of analytical science.

The transfer of laboratory based systems for use by the average person has, until recently, been the dream of Science Fiction writers but the technology has matured considerably in the past few decades and numerous commercial products are now widely available within the retail sector. The devices offer rapid response and hence proffer the possibility of immediate action (i.e. glucose measurements by diabetics) or, in some instances, an opportunity for taking more long term preventative measures (typified by weekly cholesterol measurements). They obviate the need for the transfer of the samples to the lab, the inevitable delays in

---

* E-mail address: maria.marti@ntu.ac.uk; T: +44 (0) 115 848 3218.
† E-mail address: james.davis@ntu.ac.uk.

processing and the possibility of sample degradation that can occur either in transport or storage.

The advent of domestic diagnosis as promised by such technology generates the supposition that allowing the user to actively participate in the measurement process will generate a greater degree of responsibility in the management of their health. This is typified by the analysis of heart disease biomarkers whereby the patient, rather than the healthcare provider, is given a degree of responsibility for maintaining appropriate levels of lipoproteins through dietary manipulation. Similar arguments can be made for a host of other applications – not necessarily medical. Maintaining garden fertility is a million miles from the hospital ward but the technology used to assess such is the close cousin of that being used in the latter. The basic monitoring and subsequent participatory management premise is the same irrespective of end user application.

There are however issues to be resolved – selectivity - is still a major issue as is the integration of the sensing component with the transducing hardware. In order to be usable out with the lab – the eventual devices have to be robust – in terms of the actual measurement process but also in the handling and storage by the user. The latter is seldom an issue with lab based systems where the environment is carefully controlled and the operators are assumed to have a greater degree of scientific knowledge. Compare that with the situation where the average person is conducting the analysis in their home. Composite technologies have come to the fore in both scenarios but the remit of the present review has been to examine the development of novel materials that underpin the measurement interface rather than those that simply provide the plastic shroud that protects it. A wide spectrum of methodologies has been employed in the development of portable biosensor systems but the remit of this review has been restricted to those involving predominately electrochemical transduction. At present, the latter represents the majority interest in the sensor community. Nevertheless, it is likely that the materials being discussed will also have application to the other detection methodologies.

In: Materials Science Researcher Biographical Sketches …   ISBN: 978-1-61942-153-0
Editors: Satomi Matsumoto and Ueda Iwate   © 2013 Nova Science Publishers, Inc.

Chapter 142

REVIEW ON METHODOLOGIES OF PROGRESSIVE FAILURE ANALYSIS OF COMPOSITE LAMINATES

P. F. Liu and J. Y. Zheng
Institute of Chemical Machinery and Process Equipment,
Zhejiang University, Hangzhou, China

RESEARCH SUMMARY

Stiffness degradation for laminated composites such as carbon fiber/epoxy composites is an important physical response to the damage and failure evolution under continuous or cyclic loads. The ability to predict the initial and subsequent evolution process of such damage phenomenon is essential to explore the mechanical properties of laminated composites. This chapter gives a general review on the popular methodologies which deal with the damage initiation, stiffness degradation and final failure strength of composite laminates. These methodologies include the linear/nonlinear stress calculations, the failure criteria for initial microcracking, the stiffness degradation models and solution algorithms in the progressive failure analysis. It should be pointed out that the assumption of constant damage variable which is introduced into the constitutive equations of laminated composites to simulate the stiffness degradation properties is less effective and practical than that of changed damage variable with loads in the framework of continuum damage mechanics (CDM). Also, different damage evolution laws using CDM should be assumed to describe three failure modes: fiber breakage, matrix cracking and interfacial debonding, respectively.

In: Materials Science Researcher Biographical Sketches …   ISBN: 978-1-61942-153-0
Editors: Satomi Matsumoto and Ueda Iwate   © 2013 Nova Science Publishers, Inc.

Chapter 143

OPTIC FIBRE SYSTEM FOR DAMAGE MONITORING IN COMPOSITE MATERIALS

R. de Oliveira[1] and O. Frazão[2]

[1]INEGI, Institute of Mechanical Engineering and Industrial Management, Composite Materials and Structures Research Unit, Rua Dr. Roberto Frias, Porto, Portugal
[2]INESC Porto, Instituto de Engenharia de Sistemas e Computadores do Porto, Rua do Campo Alegre, Porto, Portugal

RESEARCH SUMMARY

Composite structures integrity is sensible to service life. Their application in the aeronautical and space engineering implies the necessity to insure their integrity through non-destructive evaluations. On-line health monitoring procedure capable to detect, acquire, and identify damage in fibre reinforced plastic composite materials are necessary. Among the different non-destructive techniques, acoustic emission was chosen for its ability to detect evolutive defects during in-service life of structures. Traditionally, the AE waves are detected at the surface of the structure by piezoelectric transducers. Such transducers have some limitations (e.g. they can't be used at low/high temperature, and are sensible to electromagnetic interferences). Optic fibre sensors have revealed to be a good alternative. Due to their low dimensions they can be easily embedded in fibre reinforced composite at manufacturing.

In this chapter is discussed the use of an optic fibre system developed for damage monitoring in composite materials from the rapid release of elastic strain energy they generate, detected in the form of elastic waves. Among the different optic fibre sensors, the Fabry-Pérot interferometer is chosen for its high sensitivity to transient phenomena. The propagating acoustic emission waves induce variations of the light in the interferometer. The difficulty when using such sensor remains the phase recovery. In this study an original set-up is proposed for phase recovery based on the generation of two quadrature-shifted phase interferometric signals from two fibre Bragg gratings. The optic fibre sensor is embedded in a cross-ply carbon fibre/epoxy laminate. The optic fibre sensor system successfully detects periodic ultrasonic waves propagating into the material as well as simulated acoustic emission waves. These tests demonstrate that the optic fibre system is suitable for damage detection from acoustic emission waves.

Such in-service health monitoring methodology can be used to locate damage and to determine its severity.

In: Materials Science Researcher Biographical Sketches ...   ISBN: 978-1-61942-153-0
Editors: Satomi Matsumoto and Ueda Iwate   © 2013 Nova Science Publishers, Inc.

Chapter 144

FORMULATION OF A MACRO-ELEMENT TO ANALYZE THE MECHANICAL BEHAVIOR OF GENERAL COMPOSITE LAMINATED PLATES

Liz G. Nallim[*] *and Sergio Oller*[†]

[1]CONICET - Facultad de Ingeniería - Universidad Nacional de Salta, Salta, Argentina
[2]Departamento de Resistencia de Materiales y Estructuras en la Ingeniería, Universidad Politécnica de Cataluña, Barcelona, Spain

RESEARCH SUMMARY

A general analytical - numerical approach developed for the statical and dynamical analysis of unsymmetrically laminated plates of general quadrilateral shapes is presented in this chapter. An arbitrary quadrilateral flat laminate is mapped onto a square basic one, so that a unique macro-element is constructed for the whole plate. The Ritz method is applied to evaluate the governing equation in which all coupling effects, including those of bending and stretching, are contained. Kinematical assumptions of the Classical Lamination Plate Theory (CLPT) are considered in the equivalent single-layer laminate theories (ESL) context. The plate deflection is approximated by sets of beam characteristic orthogonal polynomials generated using the Gram-Schmidt procedure, always working in the generated macro-element.

All possible transverse boundary conditions combining with the different in-plane constraints are considered in the analysis. The convergence studies and the comparisons with results available from the literature indicate that the approach presented is reliable and accurate. Sets of numerical results are given in tabular and graphical form illustrating the influence of different number of layers, fiber stacking sequences and edge conditions on the static deflection, natural frequencies and nodal patterns of a selection of laminated plates.

---

[*] E-mail address: lnallim@unsa.edu.ar.
[†] E-mail address: sergio.oller@upc.edu.

In: Materials Science Researcher Biographical Sketches ...   ISBN: 978-1-61942-153-0
Editors: Satomi Matsumoto and Ueda Iwate   © 2013 Nova Science Publishers, Inc.

Chapter 145

DELAMINATION OF COMPOSITE STRUCTURE UNDER VARIOUS TYPES OF LOADING BY HYBRID MONGREL ELEMENTS

Nguyen Tien Duong[1] and Nguyen Dang Hung[2]
[1]Department of Welding Engineering and Metal Technology,
Hanoi University of Technology, Hanoi, Vietnam
[2]Laboratory of Aero-Spatial Techniques, University of Liege, Liege, Belgium

RESEARCH SUMMARY

The anisotropic elasticity theory and solution of Lekhnitskii for generalized plane strain state are presented. Wang's singular solution is used to determine the stress singularity order and eigen coefficients.

The stress intensity factors K_i (i = I, II and III), which characterize the toughness of the structure, are calculated. A solution is also considered by the calculation of the energy release rates (G_i and G_{total}) for delamination crack.

The local and precise evaluation of the interlaminar stresses which those of K_i, G_i and G_{total} requires a very fine mesh of finite elements near the free edges and at the crack tip of delamination.

In order to appreciably reduce the fine mesh in finite elements of pure displacement type, we undertook the development of a finite element in 2 dimensions of the mongrel type (metis element) in regular and singular stress fields. This special class of hybrid finite element assures the monotone convergence was proposed by Nguyen Dang Hung. This element has advantages of the classical finite element and the hybrid element.

A method allowing the determination of the order of the stress singularity of the delamination crack was presented. The determination of the stress singularity of the delamination is necessary to know the behavior of the stress in the vicinity of the crack tip. Results of three stress intensity factors and the energy release rates for delamination crack in composite laminates under various types of loading (axial extension, bending, twisting) are presented and compared with the literature to demonstrate the efficiency of the present method.

In: Materials Science Researcher Biographical Sketches …   ISBN: 978-1-61942-153-0
Editors: Satomi Matsumoto and Ueda Iwate   © 2013 Nova Science Publishers, Inc.

Chapter 146

THE SURFACE INTEGRITY OF COMPOSITE LAMINATES SUBJECTED TO DRILLING

A. M. Abrão[1], J. Paulo Davim[2],,*
J. C. Campos Rubio[1] and P. E. Faria[1]
[1]Department of Mechanical Engineering, University of Minas Gerais,
Belo Horizonte MG, Brazil
[2]Department of Mechanical Engineering, University of Aveiro, Aveiro, Portugal

RESEARCH SUMMARY

In general, composite laminates are produced near net shaped, thus requiring machining operations to achieve the specified dimensions/tolerances and to allow assembly. Owing to the fact that drilling is the machining operation most frequently applied to composite laminates, this chapter is focused on the influence of the machining parameters on the surface integrity of the finished component. More specifically, delamination, surface finish and the dimensional and geometric deviations induced after drilling fiber-reinforced polymeric laminates are discussed based on the cutting phenomena involved. The findings suggest that tool geometry plays a critical role on the surface integrity of machined composites and that standard drill geometries recommended for metal cutting are not suitable for this grade of materials. In addition to that, feed rate is the most relevant machining parameter affecting the integrity of fiber-reinforced polymeric composites, i.e., the higher the feed rate, the higher the damage induced.

* E-mail address: pdavim@ua.pentru. (Corresponding author).

In: Materials Science Researcher Biographical Sketches ...   ISBN: 978-1-61942-153-0
Editors: Satomi Matsumoto and Ueda Iwate   © 2013 Nova Science Publishers, Inc.

Chapter 147

FAILURE PROCESS OF CARBON FIBER COMPOSITES

*Alexander Tesar**

Institute of Construction and Architecture, Slovak Academy of Sciences,
Bratislava, Slovak Republic

RESEARCH SUMMARY

Some research results of failure behaviour of carbon fiber composites are presented. The solution of material instability on the basis of fiber kinking theory is adopted for the treatment of the failure process. The micromechanical modeling adopting the FETM-approach is used for numerical analysis of the problem. Some numerical and experimental results with actual application are submitted in order to demonstrate the efficiency of the approaches suggested.

---

* E-mail address: usarate@savba.sk.

In: Materials Science Researcher Biographical Sketches ...　　ISBN: 978-1-61942-153-0
Editors: Satomi Matsumoto and Ueda Iwate　　© 2013 Nova Science Publishers, Inc.

Chapter 148

TOWARDS DIFFUSE INTERFACE MODELS WITH A NONLINEAR POLYCRYSTALLINE ELASTIC ENERGY

Thomas Blesgen[*] *and Anja Schlomerkemper*[†]

Max Planck Institute for Mathematics in the Sciences, Leipzig, Germany

RESEARCH SUMMARY

Recently in, an extension of the Cahn-Hilliard model was derived that takes into account nonlinear elastic energies of the precipitates and includes composite laminates in the physical description. The aim of this work is to provide a basis for the further generalization of isothermal diffuse interface models, which we do by developing our methods exemplary for the Allen-Cahn/Cahn-Hilliard equations. Since segregated phases in typical physical applications are polycrystalline, it is natural to incorporate also effects present in polycrystals rather than in single crystals, leading to a polycrystalline lamination theory. To this end we recall some models and methods used in the context of polycrystalline materials and composites. Finally, we outline how the Allen-Cahn/Cahn-Hilliard model can be extended to polycrystalline geometrically linear elasticity.

[*] E-mail address: blesgen@mis.mpg.de.
[†] E-mail address: schloem@mis.mpg.de.

In: Materials Science Researcher Biographical Sketches …   ISBN: 978-1-61942-153-0

Editors: Satomi Matsumoto and Ueda Iwate   © 2013 Nova Science Publishers, Inc.

Chapter 149

CONTROL OF THE SONIC BOOM GENERATED BY A FLYING VEHICLE BY MEANS OF A CRYOGENIC IMPACT ON THE FLOW PROCESS

V. M. Fomin, V. F. Chirkashenko, A. M. Kharitonov and V. F. Volkov

Khristianovich Institute of Theoretical and Applied Mechanics,
Siberian Branch, Russian Academy of Sciences, Novosibirsk, Russia

RESEARCH SUMMARY

Cooling of surfaces of various objects is widely used in science and engineering. This process assists in formation of better characteristics of various devices, tools, and instruments by increasing the quality of their operation and reliability. On the other hand, surface cooling and supercooling can generate severe problems in operation of vehicles, sometimes leading to catastrophic situations. Therefore, despite the long story of studying the cooling processes, it is still important because of numerous applications.

The cooling processes are particularly versatile and important in aeronautics, because they affect flight safety. Aircraft icing caused by collisions of supercooled water drops with the windshield, resulting in rapid crystallization of these drops and formation of ice accretions of various shapes and sizes, is well known. This unsteady process arises when the aircraft enters clouds containing fine droplets of supercooled water in a metastable state at negative temperatures (down to $-40 \div -60°C$). In most cases, aircraft icing occurs when it flies in the atmosphere containing supercooled water drops (i.e., water in the liquid phase at negative temperatures). During their collisions with the frontal surfaces of aircraft elements, the water drops become rapidly crystallized, forming ice accretions of various shapes and sizes. Under icing conditions, ice structures are formed on the frontal surfaces of the wings, rudder and elevator, propellers, cockpit windows, navigation gauges, and blisters. Unfortunately, the mechanism of rapid crystallization of supercooled drops after their impact on the aircraft surface has not bee adequately studied yet. Despite the increasing effectiveness of various devices, icing is still a factor that exerts a substantial effect on flight safety and regularity.

Statistical data on aircraft icing situations in various geographical regions of the Earth show that icing is most probable if the aircraft flies in the temperature range from 0 to −15°C. Some cases of icing at air temperatures of −50°C and lower were registered.

Inlet channels of aircraft engines can also be subjected to icing at positive (up to +10°C) temperatures. This is explained by condensation and freezing of air moving in inlet channels. Cases of icing of supersonic inlets are also known.

At supersonic flight velocities, the temperature of inlet surfaces drastically increases and can exceed 2000°C at Mach numbers $M_\infty = 5 \div 8$. Therefore, it is necessary to cool the compression surfaces and, simultaneously study the influence of cooling on inlet performance. Hypersonic inlets are cooled to ensure their thermal protection and improve their aerodynamic characteristics. These problems were discussed in. It was demonstrated that cooling makes the laminar boundary layer on the central body more stable to developed separation and prevents upstream transfer of counter pressure, which leads to reduction and elimination of separation ahead of the inlet and to significant improvement of the throttling characteristics of the inlet.

Surface cooling at supersonic velocities exerts a considerable effect on boundary layer stability and its transition to the turbulent state. This research direction has been actively developed at the Khristianovich Institute of Theoretical and Applied Mechanics of the Siberian Branch of the Russian Academy of Sciences (ITAM SB RAS). Some results are published in. It was demonstrated in computations and experiments that surface cooling is accompanied by stabilization of the first mode of disturbances, which favors reduction of the range of unstable frequencies, and the neutral stability curve is shifted toward higher Reynolds numbers. At the same time, the second mode of disturbances (high frequencies) is destabilized, i.e., the range of unstable frequencies is expanded, moving toward higher frequencies, whereas the amplification factor increases. Surface cooling does not affect the interaction of acoustic waves with the supersonic boundary layer. Experimental data obtained agree with predictions of the hydrodynamic stability theory. When the aircraft moves with a supersonic velocity, its surfaces are subjected to considerable aerodynamic heating. Therefore, one of the key problems in creating such flying vehicles is cooling of heat-intense elements of the airframe, engine, and onboard equipment, which cannot be solved at the expense of the cooling capacity of liquid fuels, such as kerosene. Therefore, the Tupolev Joint Stock Company developed an experimental aircraft TU-155, which was adapted to use not only liquid hydrogen, but also liquefied natural gas (LNG). It should be noted that liquid hydrogen possesses extremely useful properties: high heat of combustion, tremendous cooling capacity, and environmentally friendly nature, which make it possible to improve the flight performance and to create aircraft with flight velocities M > 6. Thus, the first aircraft in the world operating on cryogenic fuels was developed.

Aerospace industry also involves the search for new material resources to create more environmentally friendly fuels that simultaneously ensure a high cooling capacity. Such fuels can be hydrocarbon gases (methane, propane, butane, etc.) obtained from natural and oil gases, and also hydrogen. These gases are rather different in terms of their physical properties, which can substantially affect the aircraft structure, propulsion, and exploitation.

The above-given examples give only limited illustrations of the spectrum of surface cooling applications and, simultaneously, stimulate the use of these processes in solving other problems. It is known, in particular, that sonic boom (SB) reduction by conventional methods based on searching for an optimal distribution of the volume and lift force along the aircraft has not yet seen much progress. The configuration of the Concorde supersonic passenger aircraft, which is close to optimal in terms of the SB signature, does not ensure an admissible SB level required by ICAO norms. As was shown in, the excess pressure level on the Earth's surface in the cruising flight of Concorde exceeds 100 Pa. Results of research aimed at the development of the supersonic passenger plane of the second generation also show that it is impossible to reach an admissible SB level generated by a conventional configuration of the aircraft with a large takeoff weight without deteriorating the lift-to-drag ratio. These and other studies dealing with passive methods of SB reduction in flight of supersonic transport planes undoubtedly show that it are necessary to search for new methods of controlling the SB parameters. The first investigations of active control of SB parameters by means of mass addition (in the form of air jets oriented with respect to the model in a certain manner) and energy addition (ensured by combustion of a hydrogen-air mixture) near the body show the prospects of this approach. Recent research in the last decade includes various methods of energy supply to a supersonic flow with the use of laser and microwave radiation, electron guns, and spark discharges, aimed at controlling the flow parameters, including the formation of a disturbed flow near the flying vehicle. At the same time, the process of energy removal with the help of cryogenic technologies offers many new possibilities of active control of the flow around the aircraft and the level of the sonic boom generated by this aircraft.

The present chapter describes the results of numerical and experimental investigations performed at ITAM SB RAS. The parameters of the SB generated by power-law bodies of revolutions were systematically studied in experiments and calculations. The result was determining a class of modified (with the help of spherical bluntness of the nose part) bodies that ensure reduction of the bow shock wave intensity, as compared with a non-blunted body with the same aspect ratio in the middle zone of the sonic boom. Cryogenic technologies of controlling the flow around the aircraft were developed to extend the length of the SB minimization region (middle zone) to distances corresponding to the cruising flight altitude. A detailed description of the experimental techniques and facilities is given. A series of experimental and numerical studies was performed, and the possibility of active controlling of SB parameters by means of surface cooling and organization of distributed injection of the coolant into the flow was demonstrated for the first time.

In: Materials Science Researcher Biographical Sketches ...   ISBN: 978-1-61942-153-0
Editors: Satomi Matsumoto and Ueda Iwate   © 2013 Nova Science Publishers, Inc.

Chapter 150

LIQUID OXYGEN MAGNETOHYDRODYNAMICS

J. C. Boulware, H. Ban,
S. Jensen and S. Wassom

Mechanical and Aerospace Engineering Dept.,
Utah State University, Logan, Utah, US

RESEARCH SUMMARY

In the cryogenic realm, liquid oxygen (LOX) possesses a natural paramagnetic susceptibility and does not require a colloidal suspension of particles for practical application as a magnetic working fluid. Commercial ferrofluids have performed well in industrial applications, but expanding their workable range to low temperatures requires a suitable selection of the carrier fluid, such as LOX. In this chapter, the equation of motion for the pure fluid is derived and applied to a slug of LOX being displaced by a pulsed magnetic field. Its theoretical performance is compared to actual experimental data with discussion on empirical parameters, sensitivity to measurement uncertainty, and geometric similarity. The 1.1 T pulse of magnetic flux density produced oscillations in the slug of 6-8 Hz, generating up to 1.4 kPa of pressure change in a closed section when the slug acted like a liquid piston. The experiments and theoretical model demonstrate that LOX could be used as a magnetic working fluid in certain applications.

In: Materials Science Researcher Biographical Sketches ...   ISBN: 978-1-61942-153-0
Editors: Satomi Matsumoto and Ueda Iwate   © 2013 Nova Science Publishers, Inc.

Chapter 151

Effect of Cryogenic Treatment on Microstructure and Mechanical Properties of Light Weight Alloys

Kaveh Meshinchi Asl[1] and Mehdi Koneshloo[2]

[1]School of Materials Science and Engineering, Clemson University, Clemson, SC, US
[2]Department of Materials Science and Engineering,
Sharif University of Technology, Tehran, Iran

Research Summary

This chapter mainly focuses on the effects of low temperature (subzero) treatments on microstructure and mechanical properties of aluminum and magnesium alloys. Deep cryogenic treatment on A319 aluminum alloy showed that the abrasion resistance of the alloy was improved after the treatment. This improvement was attributed to the strengthening of the α-aluminum matrix which slows down the propagation of the existing defects. The execution of deep cryogenic treatment on AZ91 magnesium alloy changed the distribution of β precipitates. The tiny laminar β particles almost dissolved in the microstructure and the coarse divorced eutectic β phase penetrated into the matrix. This microstructural modification resulted in a significant improvement on mechanical properties of the alloy. The steady state creep rates were measured and it was found that the creep behavior of the alloy, which is dependent on the stability of the near grain boundary microstructure, was improved by the deep cryogenic treatment. After the deep cryogenic treatment, the sliding of grain boundaries was greatly suppressed due to morphological changes. As a result, the grain boundaries are less susceptible for grain boundary sliding at high temperatures. After dry sliding wear tests were performed, the wear resistance of the alloy improved remarkably after deep cryogenic treatment.

Furthermore due to interest in the subzero treatments of steels in the past few decades, AISI H13 tool steel was chosen and cryogenic treatment at -72°C and deep cryogenic treatment at -196°C were applied and it was found that the execution of low temperature treatments on samples affected the microstructure of the H13 tool alloy to a great extent. By applying the subzero treatments, the retained austenite was transformed to martensite due to the completion of martensite transformation. The cryogenic treatment at a very low temperature and holding the samples for a long time, also lead to precipitation of more uniform and very fine carbide particles. This microstructural modification resulted in a significant improvement on mechanical properties and wear resistance of the alloy.

In: Materials Science Researcher Biographical Sketches …   ISBN: 978-1-61942-153-0
Editors: Satomi Matsumoto and Ueda Iwate   © 2013Nova Science Publishers, Inc.

Chapter 152

CRYOGENIC TREATMENT AND FATIGUE RESISTANCE

Paolo Baldissera and Cristiana Delprete

Politecnico di Torino, Corso Duca degli Abruzzi, Torino,Italy

RESEARCH SUMMARY

Among the various applications of cryogenics, the implementation of cold thermal processes with the aim of enhancing mechanical properties of materials is the most attractive from the perspective of structural component engineering design. In particular, considering the key-role played by the fatigue behavior of materials in this discipline, the development of methodologies that allow to achieve longer service life is an evergreen topic, which concerns many fields of application such as energy production and transportation. Starting from the scientific literature of the last 30 years concerning shallow and deep cryogenic treatment (SCT and DCT) and including the most recent experimental results achieved at the Politecnico di Torino, both direct and indirect evidences of an effective influence on the fatigue behavior of steels are pointed-out. Experimental methodologies and data analysis approaches are detailed with a special focus on the estimation of optimal treatment parameters. In particular, two classes of steels that show a good liability for such processes are discussed in depth: austenitic stainless steels and carburized ones. In both cases, the potential consequence in terms of reliability and service life of structural components is noticeable and can be highlighted through practical design examples (stainless steel springs and carburized gears are discussed in details). In the final part of the chapter, an overall picture of the most promising future applications is given with a particular focus on materials beyond steels such as different alloys (i.e. aluminum, magnesium, titanium), polymers and composites and in consideration of their specific fatigue mechanisms.

In: Materials Science Researcher Biographical Sketches ...   ISBN: 978-1-61942-153-0
Editors: Satomi Matsumoto and Ueda Iwate   © 2013 Nova Science Publishers, Inc.

Chapter 153

APPLICATION OF FIBER BRAGG GRATING SENSORS AT CRYOGENIC TEMPERATURES

Ines Latka, Tobias Habisreuther and Wolfgang Ecke

Institute of Photonic Technology (IPHT), Jena, Germany

RESEARCH SUMMARY

Fiber Bragg grating (FBG) sensors are well known means for the measurement of strain and temperature in broad temperature and strain ranges. The most important features of this sensor type are its small size, light weight, full electrical insulation, negligible interaction with electric and magnetic fields, and the flexible fiber leads of good thermal insulation between sensor and its interrogation unit. In particular, the low thermal conductivity of the optical fiber is an advantage when working with low temperatures. Another important feature is the possibility to include several grating sensors in the same fiber, which can later be interrogated simultaneously via wavelength multiplexing.

An FBG can be defined as a periodic modulation of the refractive index along a section of the fiber core. Such gratings can be produced by the irradiation of photosensitive silica fibers with an UV laser and an interferometer setup. The FBG reflects a wavelength, which is dependent on the period of the structure and on the effective refractive index of the fiber. Exposure to temperature or strain changes will affect the period of the structure or/and the refractive index, thereby changing the reflected wavelength. A polychromator based measurement guarantees simultaneous measurements for all sensors in the wavelength-multiplexed assembly, with equal measurement duration of typically 100 µs. Thus, it is possible to reconstruct exact strain modes or temperature distributions from the actual multi-point results. The wavelength changes can be monitored with a 1σ repeatability of about 0.1 pm.

While conventional electrical resistance strain gages show increasing cross-sensitivities to temperature and magnetic field with decreasing temperature down to liquid helium, it has been found that fiber optic Bragg grating strain sensors show negligible thermo-optic and magneto-optic effects in the cryogenic environment and they allow, therefore, reliable strain measurements.

These specific application advantages of optical fiber Bragg grating sensors at low temperatures make them attractive for structural health monitoring of cryogenic devices such as superconductive magnets. Other applications are material characterization, e.g. of superconducting materials or of structural elements, respectively. Flux pinning is one of the most fundamental and interesting properties of type II superconductors. In materials with the strongest pinning, the pinning-induced strain can be so large that it can lead to cracks in the material. With the application of FBG sensors, spatially resolved measurements of magnetostrictive effects in superconducting samples become possible. FBGs can also be used for the measurement of thermal expansion coefficients down to 4 K, or for the change of Young's modulus with respect to temperature.

In: Materials Science Researcher Biographical Sketches ...   ISBN: 978-1-61942-153-0
Editors: Satomi Matsumoto and Ueda Iwate   © 2013 Nova Science Publishers, Inc.

Chapter 154

CRYOGENIC GRINDING: APPLICATION FOR STRUCTURAL MODIFICATION AND FORMULATION DEVELOPMENT OF DRUG MOLECULES

Kunikazu Moribe, Kenjirou Higashi and Keiji Yamamoto

Graduate School of Pharmaceutical Sciences,
Chiba University, Inohana, Chuo-ku, Chiba, Japan

RESEARCH SUMMARY

Cryogenic grinding is used to modify the physicochemical properties of a solid drug. A low-crystalline or amorphous form is formed depending on grinding conditions such as temperature and grinding time. Methods used to prepare amorphous forms sometimes affect the stability and dissolution behavior of drugs, even if the powder X-ray diffraction measurement of each formulation shows a halo pattern. Grinding of a drug in the presence of excipients makes it possible to prepare drug formulations such as solid dispersions, complexes, and cocrystals. Grinding under cryogenic conditions is favorable when formulation components are not suitable for ambient temperature grinding. Grinding temperature affects the molecular states of the components of the system. The physicochemical characterization of samples prepared at different temperatures can be used to effectively determine the mechanism of complex or cocrystal formation. Drug nanoparticles with improved dispersibility and dissolution properties can be prepared by using suitable excipients. Thus, sample grinding under cryogenic conditions appears to be useful in the field of pharmaceutics.

In: Materials Science Researcher Biographical Sketches …   ISBN: 978-1-61942-153-0
Editors: Satomi Matsumoto and Ueda Iwate   © 2013 Nova Science Publishers, Inc.

Chapter 155

IMPROVEMENTS IN TOLERANCE TO CRYOPRESERVATION USING SHOOT-TIPS OF CHRYSANTHEMUM (*DENDRANTHEMA GRANDIFLORUM* KITAM.) FROM GENETICALLY MODIFIED PLANTS THAT ACCUMULATE TREHALOSE

María Teresa González-Arnao[1], José O. Mascorro-Gallardo[2], Antelmo Osorio Saenz[2], María del Rocío Valle-Sandoval[2] and Florent Engelmann[3,4]

[1]Universidad Veracruzana, Facultad de Ciencias Química, Orizaba, Estado de Veracruz, México
[2]Universidad Autónoma Chapingo, Departamento de Fitotecnia Chapingo, Estado de México, México
[3]Institut de recherche pour le développement (IRD), Montpellier, France
[4]Bioversity International, Maccarese, Rome, Italy

RESEARCH SUMMARY

Intracellular accumulation of organic osmolytes such as sucrose and trehalose is highly correlated with tolerance to stress induced by dehydration and freezing in many plants and microorganisms. Based on the existence of such protective mechanisms, we generated genetically modified lines of chrysanthemum (*Dendranthema grandiflorum* Kitam.) var. Indianapolis with induced capacity to biosynthesize trehalose, and performed cryo-preservation experiments with shoot-tips isolated from chrysanthemum *in vitro* plantlets of two transgenic lines with different endogenous accumulation of trehalose and with shoot-tips dissected from non transgenic *in vitro* plantlets. After dissection, apices were precultured on semi-solid MS medium supplemented with 0.3 M sucrose for 4 days, loaded in a 0.4 M sucrose + 2 M glycerol solution for 20–30 min and exposed to PVS2 or PVS3 vitrification solutions for 0, 20, 40 or 60 min at room temperature prior to rapid immersion in liquid nitrogen in cryovials with 1mL of the respective PVS. The highest shoot regeneration after cryopreservation was obtained following exposure to either PVS solution for 40 min. Genetically modified tissues displayed an improved tolerance to cryopreservation in comparison with non transgenic ones. Cryopreserved shoot tips from plants of transgenic lines produced 67% and 48% shoot regeneration after treatment with PVS2 and 54% and 52% with PVS3, while non-transgenic ones showed 33% shoot regeneration after treatment with PVS2 and 36% with PVS3. These results demonstrate that genetic engineering techniques can be a useful biotechnological tool to generate transgenic organisms showing improved tolerance to cryopreservation.

In: Materials Science Researcher Biographical Sketches …   ISBN: 978-1-61942-153-0

Editors: Satomi Matsumoto and Ueda Iwate   © 2013 Nova Science Publishers, Inc.

Chapter 156

CRYOGENICS VESSELS THERMAL PROFILING USING THE BOUBAKER POLYNOMIALS EXPANSION SCHEME BPES INVESTIGATION

Da Hong Zhang
South China University, Guangzhou, P.R. China

RESEARCH SUMMARY

This chapter investigates temperature dynamical profiling inside vacuum-insulated cryogenic vessels. The proposed temperature, velocity and acceleration profiles in the particular case of cylindrical geometry have been obtained through the application of the Boubaker Polynomials Expansion Scheme (BPES).

In: Materials Science Researcher Biographical Sketches ...   ISBN: 978-1-61942-153-0
Editors: Satomi Matsumoto and Ueda Iwate   © 2013 Nova Science Publishers, Inc.

Chapter 157

RESIN COMPOSITES FOR POST CEMENTATION AND CORE BUILD-UP

Juthatip Aksornmuang[*]

Department of Prosthetic Dentistry, Faculty of Dentistry,
Prince of Songkla University, Hatyai, Songkhla, Thailand

RESEARCH SUMMARY

Resin composites have been used for various purposes in restorative dentistry. Specific resin composite materials have been manufactured for the express purpose of core restorations. Currently, resin composite core material has also been recommended for luting endodontic posts due to the simplicity and homogeneity of using the same material for the post and core placement. The utilization of resin-based luting agents, both for resin cements and resin composite core materials for post cementation is reviewed in this chapter. There are three types of existing resin cements that are used for cementation of endodontic posts: etch-and-rinse, self-etch, and self-adhesive cement systems. The research results are presented to compare the bond strength values of various types of resin cements. Emphasis is placed on the use of contemporary adhesives combined with dual-cure resin composite core materials for bonding fiber posts in root canals. The bond strength data obtained from various bonding strategies are shown in this chapter. The efficiency of using the one-step and two-step self etch adhesive system for bonding to the root canal is described. In addition, the optimal bonding technique for bonding resin composites both to the fiber post surfaces and root canal dentin are revealed with the bond strength data incorporated. For core build-up materials, the issues of the polymerization mode of core build-up resin composite and incompatibility between adhesives and resin composites are discussed. This chapter also reviews the mechanical properties of resin composite core materials including the ultimate tensile strength and microhardness values of various resin composite core build-up materials obtained from the author's research. The advantages and disadvantages of the auto-mix and hand-mix resin composites are shown with verification by SEM micrographs. Particularly, the composite

---

[*] Corresponding author: Telephone/Telefax: 66-74-429874, E-mail: juthatip.a@psu.ac.th.

core materials currently available in the market with their compositions and characteristics are summarized in this chapter.

In: Materials Science Researcher Biographical Sketches ...   ISBN: 978-1-61942-153-0
Editors: Satomi Matsumoto and Ueda Iwate   © 2013 Nova Science Publishers, Inc.

Chapter 158

DESIGN AND DEVELOPMENT OF NOVEL URETHANE DIMETHACRYLATE MONOMERS FOR USE IN DENTAL COMPOSITIONS

Tinca Buruiana, Violeta Melinte and Emil C. Buruiana

Romanian Academy, Petru Poni Institute
of Macromolecular Chemistry, Iasi, Romania

RESEARCH SUMMARY

Over the past years, polymeric dental materials attained a considerable progress due to the tremendous development of multifunctionalized methacrylates, since these offer a widespread possibility to generate composite resins through a suitable choice of the monomers structure and the proportion implied in the three-dimensional network formation as well as by varying the hard inorganic filler (loading, nature, shape, size, distribution, orientation, adhesion, etc). Recent aspirations and approaches to perfect the composites structure have shown that there are difficulties in the systematic upgrading of these materials because all acrylic formulations presented a volumetric shrinkage through polymerization, accompanied by a polymer ageing. Moreover, the high percentage of nonpolymerized functions significantly affects the physical properties of the formed composites, reason for that the urethane di(meth)acrylates have been initially proposed for reducing the high viscosity of diglycidyl methacrylate of bisphenol A (BisGMA) and achieving an adequate conversion in the final resins. However, besides other characteristics (adhesion to tooth substrates, insufficient material properties, etc), minimization polymerization shrinkage and increasing the degree of (meth)acrylate conversion after ambient photopolymerization of the composite are one of the most important research tasks in this field.

From this perspective, the present review will report our results concerning the synthesis and characterization of new urethane dimethacrylate monomers with and without carboxyl groups, BisGMA analogous or liquid crystalline monomethacrylates following especially the structural/compositional effects derived from their incorporation as co-monomer candidates for formulating dental composites with different fillers, in order to elucidate the photopolymerization behaviour and the specific properties (polymerization shrinkage, morphology, hydrophilicity, mechanical parameters) of the experimental specimens. Complementary, data on the crack propagation in some composites subjected to Vickers indentation will be also critically discussed.

In: Materials Science Researcher Biographical Sketches …   ISBN: 978-1-61942-153-0
Editors: Satomi Matsumoto and Ueda Iwate   © 2013 Nova Science Publishers, Inc.

Chapter 159

DENTAL COMPOSITES WITH NANO-SCALED FILLERS

*Matthew J. Little and Hao Fong**

Department of Chemistry, South Dakota School of Mines and Technology,
Rapid City, South Dakota, US

RESEARCH SUMMARY

Developed almost half a century ago, dental composites, consisting of a polymeric resin matrix and silanized glass or ceramic fillers, presented opportunities never before equaled in modern dentistry. The resin matrix is usually cured (hardened) by photo-initiated free radical polymerization. Camphorquinone (CQ) is a commonly used visible light initiator and ethyl-4-(N,N'-dimethylamino) benzoate (4-EDMAB) is a commonly used accelerator. The monomer of 2,2'-bis-[4-(methacryloxypropoxy)-phenyl]-propane (Bis-GMA) has been widely used as the dental base monomer since it was invented. Bis-GMA is a very viscous, honey-like liquid. To improve the handling qualities, a low viscosity diluents monomer, such as tri-(ethylene glycol) dimethacrylate (TEGDMA), is added to thin the resin. In the Bis-GMA/TEGDMA dental resin systems, Bis-GMA functions to limit the volumetric shrinkage induced by photopolymerization and to enhance the resin reactivity, while TEGDMA provides for increased vinyl double bond conversion. Compared to dental amalgams, the composites possess better esthetic property, have fewer safety concerns, and show reasonably satisfactory clinical results. Consequently, the composites have been widely adopted by the dental profession as the restorative material of choice. However, current dental composites are far from ideal and/or perfect; for example, mechanical properties of the composites still require significant improvements particularly for large stress-bearing posterior restorations that involve the replacement of cusps. Herein we report that innovative dental composites reinforced with nano-scaled fillers including polyhedral oligomeric silsesquioxane (POSS), fibrillar silicate, and electrospun glass nanofibers were prepared, characterized, and evaluated. The results indicated that the incorporation of small mass fractions of nano-scaled fillers substantially improved flexural strength, elastic modulus, and work of fracture values of dental composites. The mechanical properties of the composites could be further improved by

---

* Corresponding author: Phone: 605-394-1229, Fax: 605-394-1232, E-mail: Hao.Fong@sdsmt.edu.

optimizing the chemical compositions and surface treatment methods of the nano-scaled fillers. We envision that the uniform distribution of nano-scaled fillers into dental composites could result in the development of next generation dental composites, which would be particularly useful for large posterior restorations.

In: Materials Science Researcher Biographical Sketches ...   ISBN: 978-1-61942-153-0

Editors: Satomi Matsumoto and Ueda Iwate   © 2013 Nova Science Publishers, Inc.

Chapter 160

Mapping the Structure, Composition, Properties and Dental Erosion in Human Enamel

I. M. Low, A. Alhuthali and N. Duraman

Centre for Materials Research, Dept. of Applied Physics,
Curtin University of Technology, Perth, WA, Australia

Research Summary

The structure-property relationship and dental erosion in human dental enamel composites is reviewed. The phase composition, microstructure and mechanical properties as characterized by grazing-incidence synchrotron radiation diffraction, atomic-force microscopy, scanning electron microscopy and Vickers indentation are described and discussed. The existence of distinct graded changes in crystal disorder, phase abundance, crystallite size and hardness within these enamel ceramics is highlighted. The phenomenon of load-dependent hardness in enamel but load-independent hardness in the dentine is highlighted and discussed. An in-situ monitoring technique of dental erosion in tooth enamel ceramics when immersed in soft-drinks is described. Atomic absorption results suggest that the increasing weight loss in tooth enamel during dental erosion in soft drinks can be attributed to the continuous leaching of Ca^{2+} ions, in addition to phosphorus, oxygen, and hydrogen. The effect of dental erosion on the hardness of enamel is also discussed

In: Materials Science Researcher Biographical Sketches ...   ISBN: 978-1-61942-153-0
Editors: Satomi Matsumoto and Ueda Iwate   © 2013 Nova Science Publishers, Inc.

Chapter 161

EFFECT OF FILLER CONTENT AND SIZE ON MECHANICAL PROPERTIES OF DENTAL RESIN COMPOSITES: EXPERIMENTAL AND COMPUTATIONAL INVESTIGATION

Yasuhiro Tanimoto[1], Satoshi Hirayama[2] and Yo Shibata[3]*

[1]Department of Dental Biomaterials, Nihon University
School of Dentistry at Matsudo, Matsudo, Chiba, Japan
[2]Department of Dental Caries Control and Aesthetic Dentistry, Nihon University
School of Dentistry at Matsudo, Matsudo, Chiba, Japan
[3]Department of Oral Biomaterials and Technology, Showa University
School of Dentistry, Shinagawa-ku, Tokyo, Japan

RESEARCH SUMMARY

Dental resin composites have been commonly used as restorative material for dental treatment. A resin composite is a dispersion-strengthened material composed of silica glass and dimethacrylate resin. In order to enhance the chemical bonding between the silica and matrix resin, the silica glass is treated with a silane coupling agent, which has a methacryloyl group at its terminal end. As a consequence of the bonded filler phase, these materials have much better mechanical properties than did unfilled resins.

The mechanical properties of dental resin composites such as compressive strength, diametral tensile strength, flexural strength, and fracture toughness have been experimentally studied in relation to the filler content and particle size. On the other hand, several computational studies on failure behavior of dental resin composites as determined by finite element analysis have been published.

---

* Corresponding author: Department of Dental Biomaterials, Nihon University School of Dentistry at Matsudo, 2-870-1 Sakaecho Nishi, Matsudo, Chiba 271-8587, Japan, Tel.: +81-47-360-9349, Fax: +81-47-360-9350, E-mail: tanimoto.yasuhiro@nihon-u.ac.jp.

In: Materials Science Researcher Biographical Sketches …   ISBN: 978-1-61942-153-0
Editors: Satomi Matsumoto and Ueda Iwate   © 2013 Nova Science Publishers, Inc.

Chapter 162

INHIBITION OF TELOMERASE ACTIVITY IN HL-60 CELL LINE BY METHACRYLIC MONOMERS

B. Sampaolese[1], A. Lupi[1], E. Di Stasio[2], G. E. Martorana[2], G. Gambarini[3], B. Giardina[1,2] and G. Nocca[2]*

[1]Molecular Recognition Chemistry Institute, C.N.R, Rome, Italy
[2]Institute of Biochemistry and Clinical Biochemistry,
Catholic University, Rome, Italy
[3]School of Dentistry, Sapienza University of Rome, Italy

RESEARCH SUMMARY

Methacrylic compounds, like bis-phenol A glycerolate dimethacrylate (Bis-GMA), triethyleneglycol-dimethacrylate (TEGDMA), 2-hydroxyethyl methacrylate (HEMA), urethane-dimethacrylate (UDMA) and 1,4-butanediol dimethacrylate (BDDMA) are used as polymerizable components of composite resins and some cements utilized in dentistry and in other medical fields.

After performing dental restorations, amounts of uncured monomers are released either into the oral cavity or in pulpal tissues whence they can leach into the blood circulation causing, or contributing to, local or systemic adverse effects. Since the intracellular mechanisms of the aforesaid effects are still not completely clear, many *in vitro* studies with methacrylic monomers have been performed in the attempt to explain them. These studies have underlined that monomers display genotoxic, allergenic, cytotoxic, estrogenetic and mutagenic activity. Moreover, these monomers alter lipid metabolism, glutathione concentration, reactive oxygen species production, energy metabolism cell cycle and behave as differentiating agents on human promyelocytic HL-60 cell line. The last property was especially intriguing because HL-60 cells possess high telomerase activity, a phenotype related to their immortalized status. Telomerase, adding telomeric repeats to the 3'-end of telomeres, protects chromosomes from the telomeric attrition associated with the 'end-replication problem'. Telomerase activity is present in human stem cells, progenitor cells, and

---

* Corresponding author: Email: g.nocca@rm.unicatt.it.